Macmillan McGraw-Hill

Math Connects

5

Chapter 3
Resource Masters

Macmillan/McGraw-Hill

The McGraw-Hill Companies

 Macmillan/McGraw-Hill

Send all inquiries to:
Macmillan/McGraw-Hill
8787 Orion Place
Columbus, OH 43240-4027

ISBN: 978-0-02-107274-3
MHID: 0-02-107274-4

Chapter 3 Resource Masters

Printed in the United States of America.

6 7 8 9 10 RHR 16 15 14 13 12 11

Grade 5 Chapter 3
Table of Contents

Teacher's Guide to Using the
Chapter 3 Resource Masters

The *Chapter 3 Resource Masters* includes the core materials needed for Chapter 3. These materials include worksheets, extensions, and assessment options. The answers for these pages appear at the back of this booklet.

All of the materials found in this booklet are included for viewing and printing on the *TeacherWorks Plus*™ CD-ROM.

Chapter Resources

Graphic Organizer (page 1)   This master is a tool designed to assist students with comprehension of grade-level concepts. While the content and layout of these tools vary, their goal is to assist students by providing a visual representation from which they can learn new concepts.

Student Glossary (page 2)   This master is a study tool that presents the key vocabulary terms from the chapter. You may suggest that students highlight or star the terms they do not understand. Give this list to students before beginning Lesson 3–1. Remind them to add these pages to their mathematics study notebooks.

Anticipation Guide (page 6)   This master is a survey designed for use before beginning the chapter. You can use this survey to highlight what students may or may not know about the concepts in the chapter. There is space for recording how well students answer the questions before they complete the chapter. You may find it helpful to interview students a second time, after completing the chapter, to determine their progress.

Game (page 7)   A game is provided to reinforce chapter concepts and may be used at appropriate times throughout the chapter.

Resources for Computational Lessons

Reteach   Each lesson has an associated Reteach worksheet. In general, the Reteach worksheet focuses on the same lesson content but uses a different approach, learning style, or modality than that used in the Student Edition. The Reteach worksheet closes with computational practice of the concept.

Skills Practice   The Skills Practice worksheet for each lesson focuses on the computational aspect of the lesson. The Skills Practice worksheet may be helpful in providing additional practice of the skill taught in the lesson.

Homework Practice   The Homework Practice worksheet provides an opportunity for additional computational practice. The Homework Practice worksheet includes word problems that address the skill taught in the lesson.

Problem-Solving Practice   The Problem-Solving Practice worksheet presents additional reinforcement in solving word problems that apply both the concepts of the lesson and some review concepts.

Enrich   The Enrich worksheet presents activities that extend the concepts of the lesson. Some Enrich materials are designed to widen students' perspectives on the mathematics they are learning. These worksheets are written for use with all levels of students.

Resources for Problem-Solving Strategy and Problem-Solving Investigation Lessons   In recognition of the importance of problem-solving strategies, worksheets for problem-solving lessons follow a slightly different format. For problem-solving lessons, a two-page Reteach worksheet offers a complete model for choosing a problem-solving strategy. For each Problem-Solving Strategy lesson, Reteach and Homework Practice worksheets offer reinforcement of the strategy taught in the Student Edition lesson. In contrast, the Problem-Solving

Investigation worksheets include a model strategy on the Reteach worksheets and provide problems requiring several alternate strategies on the Homework Practice and Skills Practice worksheets.

Assessment Options The assessment masters in the *Chapter 3 Resource Masters* offer a wide variety of assessment tools for monitoring progress as well as final assessment.

Individual Progress Checklist This checklist explains the chapter's goals or objectives. Teachers can record whether a student's mastery of each objective is beginning (B), developing (D), or mastered (M). The checklist includes space to record notes to parents as well as other pertinent observations.

Chapter Diagnostic Test This one-page test assesses students' grasp of skills that are needed for success in the chapter.

Chapter Pretest This one-page quick check of the chapter's concepts is useful for determining pacing. Performance on the pretest can help you determine which concepts can be covered quickly and which specific concepts may need additional time.

Mid-Chapter Test This one-page chapter test provides an option to assess the first half of the chapter. It includes free-response questions.

Quizzes Three free-response quizzes offer quick assessment opportunities at appropriate intervals in the chapter.

Vocabulary Test This one-page test focuses on chapter vocabulary. It is suitable for all students. It includes a list of vocabulary words and questions to assess students' knowledge of the words.

Oral Assessment Although this two-page test is designed to be used with all students, the interview format focuses on assessing chapter content assimilated by ELL students.

Chapter Project Rubric This one-page rubric is designed for use in assessing the chapter project. You may want to distribute copies of the rubric when you assign the project and use the rubric to record each student's chapter project score.

Foldables Rubric This one-page rubric is designed to assess the Foldables graphic organizer. The rubric is written to the students, telling them what you will be looking for as you evaluate their completed Foldables graphic organizer.

Leveled Chapter Tests

- **Form 1** assesses basic chapter concepts through multiple-choice questions and is designed for use with on-level students.

- **Form 2A** is designed for on-level students and is primarily for those who may have missed the Form 1 test. It may be used as a retest for students who received additional instruction following the Form 1 test.

- **Form 2B** is designed for students with a below-level command of the English language.

- **Form 2C** is a free-response test designed for on-level students.

- **Form 2D** is written for students with a below-level command of the English language.

- **Form 3** is a free-response test written for above-level students.

- **Extended-Response Test** is an extended response test for on-level students.

Cumulative Standardized Test Practice This three-page test, aimed at on-level students, offers multiple-choice questions and free-response questions.

Student Recording Sheet This one-page recording sheet is for the standardized test in the Student Edition.

Answers

The answers for the Anticipation Guide and Lesson Resources are provided as reduced pages with answers appearing in black. Full size line-up answer keys are provided for the Assessment Masters.

Name _____ Date _____

Graphic Organizer

Use this graphic organizer to take notes on **Chapter 3: Multiply Whole Numbers**. Fill in the missing information.

Distributive Property		_____
Factor		_____
Product		_____
Clustering		_____

Name _____ Date _____

Student-Built Glossary

This is an alphabetical list of new vocabulary terms you will learn in **Chapter 3: Multiply Whole Numbers**. As you study the chapter, complete each term's definition or description. Remember to add the page number where you found the term. Add this page to your math study notebook to review vocabulary at the end of the chapter.

Vocabulary Term	Found on Page	Defintion/ Description/ Example
Associative Property of Multiplication		
clustering		
Commutative Property of Multiplication		
Distributive Property		

2

Name _____ Date _____

Student-Built Glossary *(continued)*

factor		
Identity Property of Multiplication		
product		

Dear Family,

Today my class started **Chapter 3: Multiply Whole Numbers**. I will be learning to multiply multiples of 10, 100, and 1,000 mentally. I will also be learning to multiply whole numbers. Additionally, I will identify and use properties of multiplication, multiply whole numbers, and solve problems by using the *draw a picture strategy*. Here are my vocabulary words and an activity that we can do together.

Sincerely, _____

Key Vocabulary

Distributive Property: To multiply a sum by a number, you can multiply each addend by the same number and add the products.

Factor: A number that is multiplied by another number

Product: The result of two or more numbers that are multiplied

Activity

Find similar objects around the house. Put them together in various number groupings. Find the total number of each number group.

Books to Read

Anno's Mysterious Multiplying Jar
by Mitsumasa Anno

The Rajah's Rice
by David Barry

Amanda Bean's Amazing Dream
by Cindy Neuschwander

Estimada familia:

Hoy mi clase comenzó el **Capítulo 3, Multiplica números enteros.** Aprenderé a multiplicar múltiplos de 10, 100 y 1,000. También aprenderé a multiplicar números enteros. Además, aprenderé a identificar y a usar las propiedades de la multiplicación, a multiplicar números enteros y a resolver problemas usando la *estrategia de hacer un dibujo.* A continuación, están mis palabras del vocabulario y una actividad que podemos realizar juntos.

Sinceramente, _____

Vocabulario clave

propiedad distributiva Combina la suma y la multiplicación.

factor Números que se multiplican y dan como resultado un producto.

producto El resultado de multiplicar dos o más números.

Actividad

Busquen artículos similares en la casa. Agrúpenlos en varios números de grupos. Hallen el número total de cada número de grupos.

Libros recomendados

Anno's Mysterious Multiplying Jar
de Mitsumasa Anno

The Rajah's Rice
de David Barry

Amanda Bean's Amazing Dream
de Cindy Neuschwander

Name _____ Date _____

Anticipation Guide

Multiply Whole Numbers

STEP 1   **Before you begin Chapter 3**

- Read each statement.
- Decide whether you agree (A) or disagree (D) with the statement.
- Write A or D in the first column OR if you are not sure whether you agree or disagree, write NS (not sure).

STEP 1 A, D, or NS	Statement	STEP 2 A or D
	1. The Distributive Property combines multiplication and addition.	
	2. The product is the result of two or more numbers that are multiplied.	
	3. The Identity Property is the product of any factor and 1.	
	4. This is an example of the Commutative Property: $4 \times 5 + 8 = 4 \times 8 + 5$	
	5. The Associative Property states that the order of the factors does not change the product.	
	6. $6 \times 3 = 18$ is an example of the Distributive Property.	

STEP 2   **After you complete Chapter 3**

- Reread each statement and complete the last column by entering an A (agree) or a D (disagree).
- Did any of your opinions about the statements change from the first column?
- For those statements that you mark with a D, use a separate sheet of paper to explain why you disagree. Use examples, if possible.

3

Game

Multiplication Movement

Ready

You will need:
- A deck of cards
- Paper and pencil
- 1 number cube
- 2 index cards

Set

Draw a decimal point on each index card. Give each player 1 decimal point card. Remove the face cards and the jokers from the deck of cards. Shuffle the cards and deal each player 4 cards face down.

GO!

1. Have players place the decimal point in front of them, turn over their cards, and form a number with 1 number to the left of the decimal point and 3 numbers to the right of the decimal point.

2. Toss the number cube.

3. Use the number on the number cube to multiply the number they created. Players compare their products. Each player may switch 2 cards in her or his number to try to make the product larger.

4. Re-multiply the new numbers with the same number tossed on the number cube. The player with the larger product wins.

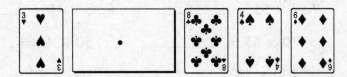

Name _____ Date _____

Reteach

Multiplication Patterns

To multiply by multiples of 10, 100, and 1,000, you can use basic facts and patterns.

Multiply 40 × 800.

Start with the basic fact.	4	×	8	= 32
Count the number of zeros in each	40	×	800	
factor and add them together.	↑		↑	

1 zero + 2 zeros = 3 zeros

Write that number of zeros in the product. 40 × 800 = 32,000

Multiply 50 × 80.

Start with the basic fact.	5	×	8	= 40
Count the number of zeros in each	50	×	80	
factor and add them together.	↑		↑	

1 zero + 1 zero = 2 zeros

Write that number of zeros in the product. 50 × 80 = 4,000

Complete.

1. 20 × 60

Basic fact: 2 × 6 = _____

Number of zeros in each factor:

_____ + 1 = _____

Product: 20 × 60 = _____

2. 9 × 80

Basic fact: _____

Number of zeros in each factor:

0 + _____ = _____

Product: _____

Find each product mentally.

3. 5 × 9 = _____

5 × 90 = _____

5 × 900 = _____

5 × 9,000 = _____

4. 3 × 6 = _____

3 × 60 = _____

3 × 600 = _____

3 × 6,000 = _____

5. 4 × 12 = _____

40 × 12 = _____

400 × 12 = _____

4,000 × 12 = _____

6. 6 × 60 = _____

60 × 60 = _____

600 × 60 = _____

6,000 × 60 = _____

7. 7 × $3 = _____

70 × $3 = _____

700 × $3 = _____

7,000 × $3 = _____

8. 5 × 40 = _____

50 × 40 = _____

500 × 40 = _____

5,000 × 40 = _____

Name _____ Date _____

Skills Practice

Multiplication Patterns

Find each product mentally.

1. 8 × 2= _____

8 × 20 = _____

8 × 200 = _____

8 × 2,000 = _____

2. 6 × 4 = _____

6 × 40 = _____

6 × 400 = _____

6 × 4,000 = _____

3. 4 × 5 = _____

4 × 50 = _____

4 × 500 = _____

4 × 5,000 = _____

4. 3 × 80 = _____

30 × 80 = _____

300 × 80 = _____

3,000 × 80 = _____

5. 5 × 60 = _____

50 × 60 = _____

500 × 60 = _____

5,000 × 60 = _____

6. 9 × $70 = _____

90 × $70 = _____

900 × $70 = _____

9,000 × $70 = _____

7. 90 × 3 = _____

8. 7 × $4,000 = _____

9. 200 × 6 = _____

10. 30 × 40 = _____

11. 600 × 70 = _____

12. 40 × 800 = _____

13. 4 × $1,000 = _____

14. 500 × 80 = _____

15. 70 × 100 = _____

16. 3 × 30 = _____

17. 5 × 1,000 = _____

18. 7 × $900 = _____

19. 50 × 80 = _____

20. 100 × 80 = _____

21. 50 × 20 = _____

Solve.

22. The 9 members of a music club in Indianapolis want to fly to New York to see several musicals. The cost of a round trip ticket is $300. How much would the airfare be altogether?

_____

23. During one week, an airport shop sold 70 New York City travel guides for $9 each. How much was the total received for the guides?

_____

Name _____ Date _____

Homework Practice

Multiplication Patterns

Find each product mentally.

1. 6 × 100 = _____

2. 8 × 300 = _____

3. 20 × 50 = _____

4. 4 × 600 = _____

5. 1,000 × 23 = _____

6. 900 × 20 = _____

7. 800 × 60 = _____

8. 12 × 60 = _____

9. 12 × 5,000 = _____

10. 500 × 90 = _____

11. 11 × 300 = _____

12. 70 × 600 = _____

13. 60 × 50 = _____

14. 80 × 200 = _____

15. 90 × 70 = _____

16. 100 × 90 = _____

17. 600 × 12 = _____

18. 40 × 90 = _____

19. 50 × 700 = _____

20. 70 × 300 = _____

21. 40 × 80 = _____

22. 70 × 110 = _____

Spiral Review

Add or subtract mentally. Use compensation. (Lesson 2–8)

23. 24 + 56 = _____

24. 33 – 12 = _____

25. 49 + 62 = _____

26. 19 + 9 = _____

27. 57 – 38 = _____

28. 310 – 218 = _____

29. 589 + 221 = _____

30. 46 + 26 = _____

31. 39 + 61 = _____

32. 472 – 28 = _____

Name _____ Date _____

Problem-Solving Practice

Multiplication Patterns

Solve.

1. There are 20 Girl Scouts. Each Girl Scout has 8 badges. How many total badges are there?

   _____

2. Lincoln Middle School ordered 60 math books. If each book costs $30, how much will the school spend?

   _____

3. Sheila is saving $8 a week for a stereo that costs $210. Will she have enough if she saves for 30 weeks?

   _____

4. A music store sells 60 CDs and 40 CD players. If each CD costs $10 and each CD player costs $30, how much did the store make?

   _____

5. To find the volume of a storage chest, Dan multiplies the chest's length times its width times its height. If the chest is 20 inches wide, 20 inches high, and 40 inches long, what is the volume of the chest?

   _____

6. Tamara is installing fence around four equal-sized square gardens. If 30 feet of fencing is needed for each garden, how many feet of fencing does Tamara need?

   _____

3-1

Enrich

Multiplication Patterns

Multiply the factors shown in the parentheses to complete these facts.

1. Adult great white sharks weigh about (2 × 800) _____ pounds and may grow to be about (4 × 5) _____ feet long.

2. The small mammal, a pygmy shrew, is only about (3 × 1) _____ inches long from head to tail.

3. The largest mammal is the blue whale. Newborn calves weigh about (20 × 300) _____ pounds. The heaviest adult caught weighed more than (50 × 7,000) _____ pounds.

4. The bat with the largest wingspan is the Bismarck flying fox. Its wingspan may be about (10 × 6) _____ inches long.

5. The largest carnivore, the polar bear, can weigh as many as (30 × 40) _____ pounds and have a nose-to tail length of about (5 × 20) _____ inches.

6. The fastest recorded speed of a kangaroo is (8 × 5) _____ miles per hour.

7. In the 1950s, an Arctic tern flew the longest distance ever recorded for a bird, (700 × 20) _____ miles.

8. In 1989, scientists recorded an elephant seal diving about (7 × 700) _____ feet.

9. The largest game preserve in the world is Estosha National Park in Namibia. It covers about (50 × 800) _____ square miles.

10. The Monterey Bay Aquarium in California has more than (600 × 600) _____ specimens of animals and plants.

Name _____ Date _____

Reteach

The Distributive Property

The Distributive Property combines addition and multiplication. To mulitiply a sum by a number, multiply each addend of the sum by the number. Then add.

Multiply 3 × 26.   Multiply and add (3 × 20) + (3 × 6).

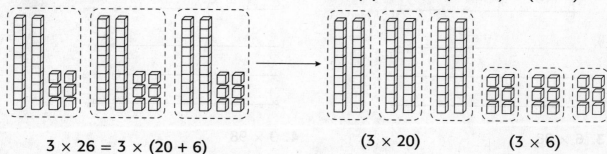

3 × 26 = 3 × (20 + 6)   (3 × 20)   (3 × 6)

$$3 \times 26 = 3 \times (20 + 6)$$
$$= (3 \times 20) + (3 \times 6)$$
$$= 60 + 18$$
$$= 78$$

Rewrite each expression using the Distributive Property. Then evaluate.

1. 3 × (15 + 6)

_____

_____

2. 6 × (14 + 3)

_____

_____

Find each product mentally using the Distributive Property. Show the steps that you used.

3. 2 × 48

_____

_____

4. 3 × 88

_____

_____

Name _____ Date _____

Skills Practice

The Distributive Property

Find each product mentally using the Distributive Property. Show the steps that you used.

1. 7 × 19

_____

_____

_____

_____

2. 2 × 27

_____

_____

_____

_____

3. 6 × 88

_____

_____

_____

4. 9 × 98

_____

_____

_____

Rewrite each expression using the Distributive Property. Then evaluate.

5. 3 × 13

_____

6. 8 × 68

_____

7. 7 × 32

_____

8. 9 × 35

_____

9. 8 × 17

_____

10. 4 × 71

_____

Solve.

11. Each of 6 hikers were allowed to bring 24 pounds of gear on a cross-country hike. How many pounds of gear was that altogether?

_____

12. The hikers plan to travel an average of 12 miles each day for 9 days. How many miles do they plan to travel in all?

_____

Name _____ Date _____

Homework Practice

The Distributive Property

Rewrite each expression using the Distributive Property. Then evaluate.

1. $3 \times (40 + 6)$

2. $6 \times (60 + 5)$

Find each product mentally using the Distributive Property. Show the steps that you used.

3. 28×6

4. 6×34

5. 35×7

6. 3×72

7. Mrs. Robertson bought 7 tickets for the school play on Monday and 5 tickets on Tuesday. Each ticket was $6. How much did she spend on the tickets? Show how you can use the Distributive Property.

8. In each package of school supplies there are 3 notebooks and 2 pencils. If you have 42 packages, how many notebooks and pencils do you have altogether? Use the Distributive Property and show your steps.

Spiral Review

Find each product mentally. (Lesson 3–1)

9. 10×18

10. 24×60

11. 300×9

12. 50×15

Name _____ Date _____

Problem-Solving Practice

The Distributive Property

Solve.

1. Ray needs to multiply 5 x 26 to find the area of a rectangle. To use the distributive property, how would you fill in the blanks?

$$5 \times 26 = 5 \times (\underline{\hspace{1cm}} + 6)$$
$$= (5 \times \underline{\hspace{1cm}}) + (5 \times 6)$$
$$= \underline{\hspace{1cm}} + 30$$
$$= \underline{\hspace{1cm}}$$

2. To multiply 8 x 14, Jana used the distributive property. Fill in the blanks to show what she did:

$$8 \times 14 = 8 \times (10 + \underline{\hspace{1cm}})$$
$$= (8 \times \underline{\hspace{1cm}}) + (8 \times 4)$$
$$= \underline{\hspace{1cm}} + 32$$
$$= \underline{\hspace{1cm}}$$

3. Four friends went out to dinner. To cover dinner, tax, and tip, each person paid $18. How much did they pay altogether?

_____

4. The fifth-grade classes at Wilcox Elementary School are reading books during the summer. There are 76 students, and each is supposed to read 4 books. How many books will the students read in all?

_____

5. The four Boy Scout troops in Carver City sold 1,238 buckets of popcorn to raise money. If each bucket costs $4, how much money did the troops raise?

_____

6. James builds and sells furniture. Last month he sold 9 bookcases and 6 coffee tables. If each bookcase costs $310, and each coffee table costs $275, how much did James make?

_____

Enrich

The Distributive Property and Subtraction

The Distributive Property can also be used to combine subtraction and multiplication. To multiply the difference of two numbers by a number, multiply each term in the parentheses by the number. Then subtract.

$3 \times (5 - 2) = (3 \times 5) - (3 \times 2)$ Use the Distributive Property to rewrite the expression.

$\qquad = 15 - 6$ Multiply the numbers in parentheses.

$\qquad = 9$ Subtract.

You can use the Distributive Property and subtraction to find a product like 2×79 mentally.

$2 \times 79 = 2 \times (80 - 1)$ Write 79 as $80 - 1$.

$\qquad = (2 \times 80) - (2 \times 1)$ Distributive Property

$\qquad = 160 - 2$ Find 2×80 and 2×1 mentally.

$\qquad = 158$ Find $160 - 2$ mentally.

Rewrite each expression using the Distributive Property. Then evaluate.

1. $3 \times (20 - 1)$ _____

2. $2 \times (10 - 1)$ _____

3. $5 \times (30 - 2)$ _____

Find each product mentally using the Distributive Property and subtraction. Show the steps that you used.

4. 2×29 **5.** 3×48

Name _____ Date _____

Reteach

Estimate Products

To estimate a product, round each number. Then use a basic fact and a
multiplication pattern to multiply mentally.

Estimate 27 × 643.   Estimate 54 × 761

Round each number
to its greatest place.   27 × 643   54 × 761
                          ↓   ↓   ↓   ↓

Write the basic fact.   **30** × **600** = **18**,000   **50** × **800** = **40**,000
Then, write the same   ↑   ↑   ↑   ↑   ↑   ↑
number of zeros in   1 zero + 2 zeros = 3 zeros   1 zero + 2 zeros = 3 zeros
the product as are in
both factors.

Estimate by rounding. Show your work.

1. 54   ×   68   **2.** 61   ×   239
        ↓   ↓   ↓   ↓

_____ × _____ = _____   _____ × _____ = _____

3. 697 ×   43   **4.** 364 ×   28
        ↓   ↓   ↓   ↓

_____ × _____ = _____   _____ × _____ = _____

5. 8 × 674   **6.** 9 × 458

_____   _____

7. 43 × 104   **8.** 19 × 74

_____   _____

9. 84 × 13   **10.** 21 × 663

_____   _____

11. 38 × 573   **12.** 18 × 264

_____   _____

13. 184 × 48   **14.** 26 × 904

_____   _____

Name _____ Date _____

Skills Practice

Estimate Products

Estimate by rounding. Show your work.

1. 34 × 10 _____

2. 59 × 32 _____

3. 446 × 682 _____

4. 21 × 663 _____

5. 98 × 32 _____

6. 91 × 32 _____

7. 334 × 847 _____

8. 929 × 8 _____

9. 43 × 58 _____

10. 186 × 92 _____

11. 342 × 86 _____

12. 396 × 23 _____

13. 8,547
   × 836

14. 603
   × 29

15. 408
   × 46

16. 3,045
   × 38

Estimate by using compatible numbers. Show your work.

17. 6 × 24 _____

18. 8 × 48 _____

19. 12 × 26 _____

20. 12 × 52 _____

21. 110 × 97 _____

22. 120 × 11 _____

Solve.

23. Tickets to a basketball game cost $22 each. Mr. Reynolds bought 17 tickets to give away as prizes at an assembly. About how much did the tickets cost altogether?

_____

24. There are 514 students at Scioto Elementary. Each of the students donated 7 food items for a charity food drive. About how many items were collected altogether?

_____

Name _____ Date _____

Homework Practice

Estimate Products

Estimate by rounding. Show your work.

1. 542
   × 38

2. 821
   × 14

3. 726
   × 38

4. 174
   × 73

5. 2,862
   × 143

6. 12,649
   ×   382

7. 69,238
   ×   54

8. 10,405
   ×   632

9. 14 × 77 _____

10. 34 × 873 _____

11. 469 × 18 _____

12. 89 × 806 _____

13. 47 × 962 _____

14. 3,721 × 499 _____

15. 198 × 2,203 _____

16. 3,926 × 198 _____

Spiral Review

Rewrite each expression using the Distributive Property. Then evaluate. (Lesson 3–2)

17. 6 × (10 + 5)

18. 4 × (30 + 6)

19. 3 × (30 + 8)

20. 7 × (40 + 6)

21. 2 × (10 + 7)

22. 6 × (40 + 8)

Name _____ Date _____

Problem-Solving Practice

Estimate Products

Solve.

1. Val bought 12 DVDs at $18 each. Estimate the total cost of the DVDs.

   _____

2. Eric's dog weighs 27 pounds, Tina's dog weighs 33 pounds, and Emir's dog weighs 29 pounds. Estimate the total weight of all three dogs.

   _____

3. On a cross-country vacation, Maria filled her 14-gallon gas tank 11 times. About how many gallons of gas did she put in the tank altogether?

   _____

4. Sven went on an 8 day vacation to Hong Kong. He took enough money with him so that he could spend $73 per day. About how much money did he take on vacation?

   _____

5. Sherry has a jogging route through her neighborhood. She ran this route for 22 days in April, 20 days in May, and 19 days in June. Estimate the total number of days she ran.

   _____

6. Klara is visiting relatives in Norway and then Sweden. First, she exchanged $184 U.S dollars for Norwegian kroner. Then she exchanged $192 for Swedish krona. Finally, she exchanged another $212 for Swedish krona. About how much did she exchange altogether?

   _____

Enrich

Estimate Products

Choose a factor from the box to give each estimated product. You can use a number more than once.

224	**789**	**17**	**322**
72	**9**	**495**	**914**

1. 483 × _____
About 150,000

2. 68 × _____
About 4,900

3. 196 × _____
About 160,000

4. 213 × _____
About 100,000

5. 14 × _____
About 100

6. 287 × _____
About 60,000

7. 12 × _____
About 200

8. 28 × _____
About 15,000

9. 23 × _____
About 18,000

10. 96 × _____
About 2,000

11. 2 × 24 × _____
About 45,000

12. 28 × _____ × 8
About 240,000

Look at the numbers in the box.

13. Which two factors would give the least product? _____

14. Which three factors would give the greatest product?

_____

_____

Name _____ Date _____

Reteach

Multiply by One-Digit Numbers

Find 32×6.

Estimate: $32 \times 6 = 180$

Step 1	Step 2

Multiply the ones.

$$\begin{array}{r} 1 \\ 32 \\ \times\ 6 \\ \hline 2 \end{array}$$ $6 \times 2 = 12$ ones

Multiply the tens.

$$\begin{array}{r} 1 \\ 32 \\ \times\ 6 \\ \hline 192 \end{array}$$ $6 \times 3 = 18$ tens

$18 + 1 = 19$ tens

The product is 192. This is close to the estimate of 180, so the answer is reasonable.

Multiply.

1. $\begin{array}{r} 53 \\ \times\ 4 \\ \hline \end{array}$ **2.** $\begin{array}{r} 26 \\ \times\ 3 \\ \hline \end{array}$ **3.** $\begin{array}{r} 38 \\ \times\ 5 \\ \hline \end{array}$ **4.** $\begin{array}{r} 47 \\ \times\ 4 \\ \hline \end{array}$

5. $\begin{array}{r} 12 \\ \times\ 3 \\ \hline \end{array}$ **6.** $\begin{array}{r} 28 \\ \times\ 6 \\ \hline \end{array}$ **7.** $\begin{array}{r} 144 \\ \times\ 3 \\ \hline \end{array}$ **8.** $\begin{array}{r} 615 \\ \times\ 4 \\ \hline \end{array}$

9. $\begin{array}{r} 262 \\ \times\ 5 \\ \hline \end{array}$ **10.** $\begin{array}{r} 811 \\ \times\ 2 \\ \hline \end{array}$ **11.** $\begin{array}{r} 501 \\ \times\ 6 \\ \hline \end{array}$ **12.** $\begin{array}{r} 149 \\ \times\ 7 \\ \hline \end{array}$

13. 5×78 **14.** 24×6 **15.** 704×3 **16.** 8×92

_____   _____   _____   _____

Name _____ Date _____

Skills Practice

Multiply by One-Digit Numbers

Multiply.

1. 83
   × 5

2. 66
   × 6

3. 32
   × 4

4. 44
   × 3

5. 56
   × 5

6. 14
   × 7

7. 28
   × 4

8. 89
   × 2

9. 557
   × 9

10. 732
    × 6

11. 645
    × 3

12. 312
    × 2

13. 564
    × 4

14. 623
    × 7

15. 769
    × 3

16. 293
    × 6

17. 4×39

18. 19×8

19. 344×7

20. 3×51

_____

_____

_____

_____

21. 2×99

22. 63×3

23. 519×4

24. 4×89

_____

_____

_____

_____

25. 2×67

26. 42×5

27. 716×8

28. 6×191

_____

_____

_____

_____

29. The math club at Southview Elementary School sold 443 rolls of wrapping paper during the holiday fundraiser. If the price of each roll was $4, how much money did they earn?

_____

30. Andrea made 28 flowerpots to sell at the craft fair. Jenna made twice as many flowerpots. How many flower pots does Jenna have?

_____

Name _____ Date _____

Homework Practice

Multiply by One-Digit Numbers

Multiply.

1. 47×3 **2.** 28×2 **3.** 65×5 **4.** 41×4

_____   _____   _____   _____

5. 6×37 **6.** 25×8 **7.** 94×7 **8.** 4×38

_____   _____   _____   _____

9. 249×6 **10.** 326×2 **11.** 3×547 **12.** 683×3

_____   _____   _____   _____

13. $\begin{array}{r} 552 \\ \times\ 3 \\ \hline \end{array}$ **14.** $\begin{array}{r} 243 \\ \times\ 4 \\ \hline \end{array}$ **15.** $\begin{array}{r} 671 \\ \times\ 7 \\ \hline \end{array}$ **16.** $\begin{array}{r} 342 \\ \times\ 2 \\ \hline \end{array}$

17. $\begin{array}{r} 128 \\ \times\ 6 \\ \hline \end{array}$ **18.** $\begin{array}{r} 444 \\ \times\ 5 \\ \hline \end{array}$ **19.** $\begin{array}{r} 831 \\ \times\ 7 \\ \hline \end{array}$ **20.** $\begin{array}{r} 756 \\ \times\ 2 \\ \hline \end{array}$

Spiral Review

Estimate by rounding. Show your work. (Lesson 3–3)

21. $\begin{array}{r} 107 \\ \times\ 54 \\ \hline \end{array}$ **22.** $\begin{array}{r} 38 \\ \times\ 7 \\ \hline \end{array}$ **23.** $\begin{array}{r} 602 \\ \times\ 14 \\ \hline \end{array}$ **24.** $\begin{array}{r} 68 \\ \times\ 69 \\ \hline \end{array}$

25. $\begin{array}{r} 42 \\ \times\ 51 \\ \hline \end{array}$ **26.** $\begin{array}{r} 216 \\ \times\ 7 \\ \hline \end{array}$ **27.** $\begin{array}{r} 19 \\ \times\ 19 \\ \hline \end{array}$ **28.** $\begin{array}{r} 401 \\ \times\ 33 \\ \hline \end{array}$

3-4

Problem-Solving Practice

Multiply by One-Digit Numbers

1. Karen and Anthony are setting up rows for the piano recital. They set up 22 rows with 6 chairs in each row. How many total people will the rows seat?

   _____

2. Each student in Mrs. Henderson's science class brought in 3 books for the book donation. If there are 25 students in the class, how many total books did they collect?

   _____

3. There are 36 teams in the baseball league. Each team has 9 players on its roster. How many total players are there?

   _____

4. Alex, Brianna, and Jonathan each have $29 to spend on a birthday gift for their mother. How much money do they have in all?

   _____

5. The Community Center purchased 7 new exercise machines for the gym. Each machine cost $269. What was the total cost?

   _____

6. One city bus can carry 72 passengers. Will three city buses be able to carry 250 passengers? Explain.

   _____

Name _____ Date _____

Enrich

The Greatest Product Game

The goal of this game is to make up the greatest product.

Get Ready!

Players: 2 to 4
You Will Need: 10 index cards

Get Set!

- Write a different digit from 0 to 9 on each card.

- Mix up the cards. Then place the cards in a pile facedown.

- Each player should draw four boxes on a piece of paper as shown.

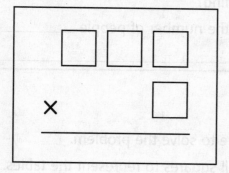

Go!

- Each player takes a turn choosing a card.

- The player writes the digit on the card in one of the boxes on his or her paper. Players may not move digits after they have placed them in a box.

- When all the boxes are full, players should find their products.

- The player with the greatest product is the winner.

Name _____ Date _____

Reteach

Problem-Solving Strategy: Draw a picture

You are making a seating chart for a math center. If one person can sit on each side of a square table, how many people can sit at four tables pushed together in a square?

Step 1 Understand	**Be sure you understand the problem.** Read carefully. What do you know? • There are _____ square tables. • _____ can sit on each side of a square table. What do you need to find? • You need to find the number of people _____ _____
Step 2 Plan • Draw a Picture • Guess and Check • Work Backward	**Make a plan.** Choose a strategy. You can draw a picture to solve the problem. You can use four small squares to represent the tables. You can use a circle to represent each chair.

Name _____ Date _____

Reteach
Problem-Solving Strategy

Draw a picture.

Step 3 Solve	Draw four small squares so that they form one large square.
	Draw one circle at each exposed edge of each small square.
	How many people can sit at four tables pushed together in a square?
	_____
Step 4 Check	**Is the solution reasonable?**
	Reread the problem.
	Have you answered the question? _____
	How can you decide if your results are reasonable?
	_____
	_____
	_____
	_____
	_____

Solve.

1. A restaurant has some circular tables and three large square tables. Two people can sit on each side of a large square table. If the three large square tables are pushed together to form a rectangle, how many people can sit at the rectangle?

2. A house has a rectangular porch that is 15 feet by 20 feet. One of the long sides of the porch is connected to the house. The other sides of the porch have a 2-foot high railing. What is the total length of the railing?

_____

3-5

Skills Practice

Problem-Solving Strategy: Draw a picture

Solve. Use the *draw a picture* strategy.

1. Maria wants to tack three rectangular pictures in a row on the bulletin board. The edges of the pictures can overlap. Maria wants to put a tack in each corner of each picture. How many tacks does she need?

_____

2. Jack builds a patio from square tiles that are 2 feet on each side. The patio is 10 feet by 16 feet. How many tiles does Jack need in order to build the patio?

_____

3. Howard leaves the dock and sails 2.5 miles west. He turns south and sails 3.5 miles. Then he turns east and sails 2.5 miles. In what direction should Howard turn if he wants to use the most direct route to return to the dock? If Howard uses this route, how many miles will he have sailed in all?

_____

4. The main lawn of a college is a rectangle with one building on each side. There is a path from each building to each of the other buildings. How many paths are there?

_____

5. Akira cut triangles of the same size out of different colors of cloth. She is going to use the pieces to make a quilt. She places the triangles together around one point until they form a hexagon. How many of the triangles did she have to use?

_____

6. For every two steps her dad takes, Heidi takes 4 steps. How many steps will she takes if her dad takes 30 steps?

_____

Name _____ Date _____

Homework Practice

Problem-Solving Strategy: Draw a picture

Solve. Use the *draw a picture* strategy.

1. Gregory arranges eight identical cubes into one large cube on a table. How many sides of the small cubes can he see?

   _____

2. Al walks 3 blocks north, 2 blocks east, 3 blocks north, and 3 blocks east to get to the theater. Will the path home be any shorter if he walks south to his street, then west to his house? Why?

   _____

3. Sandy's classroom has tables that are shaped like rectangles. Three of the tables are placed together in a U-shape. One student can sit at the short side of each rectangle or at the end of a table. Two students can sit at the long side of each rectangle. No students sit along the "inside" of the U-shape. How many students can sit at the tables the way they are arranged?

   _____ students

4. Valerie is making coasters for her mother's craft booth. For each coaster, she uses a square of cork and four pieces of wood to glue along the edges. If she has 25 pieces of cork and 92 pieces of wood, how many coasters can she make?

   _____

   Will she run out of the cork first or the wood?

   _____

Estimate. Then Multiply. (Lesson 3–4)

5. 68
   × 4

6. 59
   × 6

7. 519
   × 3

8. 874
   × 2

9. 338
   × 5

10. 902
    × 3

Enrich

Exponents

While working on a family tree project to trace his family's roots, Tim wanted to know how many great-great-grandparents he has.

Family Members	Parents	Grandparents	Great-grandparents	Great-great-grandparents
Number	2	$2 \times 2 = 4$	$2 \times 2 \times 2 = 8$	$2 \times 2 \times 2 \times 2 = 16$

So, Tim has $2 \times 2 \times 2 \times 2$ or 16 great-great-grandparents.

When a product like $2 \times 2 \times 2 \times 2$ has identical factors, you can use an exponent to write the product. An **exponent** describes how many times a number is used as a factor.

2 factors

$2 \times 2 = 2^2$

Exponent is 2.

3 factors

$2 \times 2 \times 2 = 2^3$

Exponent is 3.

4 factors

$2 \times 2 \times 2 \times 2 = 2^4$

Exponent is 4.

Rewrite each product using an exponent. Then evaluate.

1. $3 \times 3 \times 3 \times 3$ _____

2. $5 \times 5 \times 5$ _____

3. $4 \times 4 \times 4 \times 4 \times 4$ _____

4. $2 \times 2 \times 2 \times 2 \times 2 \times 2 \times 2$ _____

Rewrite each as a multiplication expression. Then evaluate.

5. 9^2 _____

6. 6^5 _____

7. 10^3 _____

8. 3^6 _____

ALGEBRA Find each missing number.

9. $7^{\square} = 49$ _____

10. $\square^2 = 64$ _____

11. $\square^5 = 32$ _____

12. $5^{\square} = 625$ _____

13. $\square^1 = 15$ _____

14. $12^{\square} = 1{,}728$ _____

Name _____ Date _____

Reteach

Multiply by Two-Digit Numbers

Find 265 × 21.
Estimate: 300 × 20 = 6,000

Step 1 **Multiply the ones.**	**Step 2** **Multiply the tens.**	**Step 3** **Add.**
265 × 21 265 265 × 1 = 265	265 × 21 265 265 × 20 = 5,300	265 × 21 265 5300 265 + 5,300 = 5,565 5,565

So, 265 × 21 = 5,565.

Multiply.

1.	45 × 12	2.	68 × 33	3.	57 × 19	4.	24 × 39	5.	72 × 46

6.	68 × 34	7.	25 × 25	8.	82 × 58	9.	93 × 37	10.	81 × 93

11.	364 × 87	12.	617 × 62	13.	703 × 29	14.	548 × 95	15.	277 × 38

16.	229 × 43	17.	326 × 55	18.	449 × 39	19.	622 × 12	20.	882 × 59

Name _____ Date _____

Skills Practice

Multiply by Two-Digit Numbers

Multiply.

1. $32 \times 517 =$ _____

2. $466 \times 21 =$ _____

3. $83 \times 13 =$ _____

4. $43 \times 65 =$ _____

5. $458 \times 26 =$ _____

6. $329 \times 72 =$ _____

7. $601 \times 24 =$ _____

8. $728 \times 68 =$ _____

9. $188 \times 46 =$ _____

10. $250 \times 27 =$ _____

11. $45 \times 371 =$ _____

12. $70 \times 686 =$ _____

13.
$$\begin{array}{r} 67 \\ \times\ 211 \\ \hline \end{array}$$

14.
$$\begin{array}{r} 30 \\ \times\ 456 \\ \hline \end{array}$$

15.
$$\begin{array}{r} 170 \\ \times\ 55 \\ \hline \end{array}$$

16.
$$\begin{array}{r} 824 \\ \times\ 19 \\ \hline \end{array}$$

17.
$$\begin{array}{r} 345 \\ \times\ 42 \\ \hline \end{array}$$

18.
$$\begin{array}{r} \$740 \\ \times\ 16 \\ \hline \end{array}$$

19.
$$\begin{array}{r} 92 \\ \times\ 301 \\ \hline \end{array}$$

20.
$$\begin{array}{r} 262 \\ \times\ 39 \\ \hline \end{array}$$

21.
$$\begin{array}{r} 114 \\ \times\ 48 \\ \hline \end{array}$$

22.
$$\begin{array}{r} 653 \\ \times\ 20 \\ \hline \end{array}$$

23.
$$\begin{array}{r} 49 \\ \times\ 700 \\ \hline \end{array}$$

24.
$$\begin{array}{r} 318 \\ \times\ 52 \\ \hline \end{array}$$

25.
$$\begin{array}{r} 202 \\ \times\ 96 \\ \hline \end{array}$$

26.
$$\begin{array}{r} 79 \\ \times\ 349 \\ \hline \end{array}$$

27.
$$\begin{array}{r} 26 \\ \times\ 781 \\ \hline \end{array}$$

28.
$$\begin{array}{r} 176 \\ \times\ 45 \\ \hline \end{array}$$

29.
$$\begin{array}{r} 500 \\ \times\ 19 \\ \hline \end{array}$$

30.
$$\begin{array}{r} 241 \\ \times\ 67 \\ \hline \end{array}$$

31.
$$\begin{array}{r} 82 \\ \times\ 820 \\ \hline \end{array}$$

32.
$$\begin{array}{r} 199 \\ \times\ 36 \\ \hline \end{array}$$

Solve.

33. A basketball player scored an average of 23 points per game. He played 82 games during the season. How many points did he score that season?

_____

34. A basketball arena has 36 sections of seats. Each section contains 784 seats. How many people can the arena seat?

_____

Homework Practice

Multiply by Two-Digit Numbers

Multiply.

1. 142 × 65 = _____

2. 407 × 73 = _____

3. $396 × 84 = _____

4. 862 × 29 = _____

5. 64 × 981 = _____

6. 69 × 46 = _____

7. 57 × $37 = _____

8. 656 × 23 = _____

9. 390 × 48 = _____

10. 357 × 54 = _____

11. 378 × 76 = _____

12. 476 × 93 = _____

13. 73 × $547 = _____

14. 326 × 57 = _____

15. 318 × 21 = _____

16. 215 × 58 = _____

17. 19 × $739 = _____

18. 862 × 12 = _____

19. 84 × 119 = _____

20. 37 × 208 = _____

21. 239 × 17 = _____

22. 926 × 60 = _____

23. 85 × 63 = _____

24. 209 × 75 = _____

25. 45 × 306 = _____

26. 443 × 19 = _____

Spiral Review

Solve. Use the *draw a picture* strategy. (Lesson 3–5)

27. Tulips are planted every 4 feet around the outside edge of a rectangular garden. If the sides of the garden measure 16 feet and 12 feet, how many total tulips are there?

_____

28. Jill has 5 pictures to hang on her wall. She wants to hang one picture in the center and the other 4 at the corners of the center picture. If the picture in the center remains the same, how many different ways can she hang the other pictures?

_____

Name _____ Date _____

Problem-Solving Practice

Multiply by Two-Digit Numbers

Solve.

1. Gary and Cedric are taking a 14-day road trip. They plan to drive 130 miles each day. How many miles would this be?

   _____

2. This summer, Jane worked for 10 weeks at her mother's book store. She earned $150 per week. How much did Jane earn?

   _____

3. The owners of Pizza Palace, a new restaurant, need to order furniture for their dining room. They need 26 tables and 120 chairs. How much will the tables and chairs cost if each table costs $43 and each chair costs $22?

   _____

4. For his job, Robert flies from Dallas, Texas, to Austin, Texas 25 times a year. If the round-trip flight between the two cities is 362 miles, how many total miles does Robert fly in a year?

   _____

5. Emily has a compact car that gets 38 miles per gallon of gas. Marcello's station wagon gets 29 miles per gallon. Emily's car holds 12 gallons of gas and Marcello's holds 15 gallons. Who can travel farther on a full tank of gas?

   _____

6. Theresa commutes to work 16 days each month. She travels 56 miles round trip. Carl commutes to work 20 days each month; he also travels 56 miles round trip. Theresa works 12 months of the year, and Carl works 11 months. Who travels more in one year?

   _____

Name _____ Date _____

Enrich

Multiply by Two-Digit Numbers

Play a multiplication game with a partner.

How to Play

- Choose a number from one of the circles and from one of the squares. Use the numbers to write a number sentence to fit each description below. Then find the product of the numbers.
- Work quickly. Your partner will record the time you used to finish the exercise.
- Switch roles. The player who uses less time wins the game.

1. the least product

_____

2. the greatest product

_____

3. two different products with a zero in the ones place

_____

4. the greatest product with an 8 in the ones place

_____

5. the least product with a 9 in the ones place

_____

6. the product with a 3 as the first and last digit

_____

7. two different products between 30,000 and 40,000

_____

8. the product closest to 60,000

_____

9. the product closest to 300,000

_____

532

83

2,178   57

9

357

921

28

6

7,059

72

45   42,133

26,041

Your time: _____   Your partner's time: _____

Name _____ Date _____

Reteach

Multiplication Properties

You can use these multiplication properties to find products mentally.

Commutative Property	Associative Property	Identity Property
The order of the factors does not change the product.	The way the factors are grouped does not change the product.	The product of any number and 1 is that number.
$25 \times 4 = 4 \times 25$ $100 = 100$	$(9 \times 4) \times 5 = 9 \times (4 \times 5)$ $36 \times 5 = 9 \times 20$ $180 = 180$	$87 \times 1 = 87$ $1 \times 6.5 = 6.5$

Identify the multiplication property used to rewrite each problem.

1. $(3 \times 5) \times 2 = 3 \times (5 \times 2)$

_____

2. $6 \times 2 \times 18 = 6 \times 18 \times 2$

_____

3. $13 \times 24 \times 9 = 9 \times 24 \times 13$

_____

4. $(15 \times 6) \times 3 = 15 \times (6 \times 3)$

_____

Use properties of multiplication to find each product mentally. Show your steps and identify the properties that you used.

5. $25 \times 9 \times 4$

_____

_____

_____

6. $(19 \times 5) \times 2$

_____

_____

_____

7. $9 \times 29 \times 0$

_____

_____

_____

8. $(4 \times 15) \times 2$

_____

_____

_____

38

Name _____ Date _____

Skills Practice

Multiplication Properties

Identify the multiplication property used to rewrite each problem.

1. $(185 \times 6) \times \underline{\hspace{1cm}} = 185 \times (6 \times 2)$

_____

2. $9 \times (60 + 7) = (\underline{\hspace{0.5cm}} \times 60) + (9 \times 7)$

_____

3. $124 \times \underline{\hspace{1cm}} = 14 \times 124$

_____

4. $3.41 \times \underline{\hspace{1cm}} = 3.41$

_____

**Use properties of multiplication to find each product mentally.
Show your steps and identify the properties that you used.**

5. $5 \times 24 \times 2$

_____

_____

_____

6. $200 \times (4 \times 7)$

_____

_____

_____

7. $483 \times 10 \times 1$

_____

_____

_____

8. $5 \times 3 \times 20$

_____

_____

_____

Name _____ Date _____

Homework Practice

Multiplication Properties

Identify the multiplication property used to rewrite each problem.

1. $(81 \times 4) \times 5 = 81 \times (4 \times 5)$

_____

2. $(28 \times 7) \times 16 = 28 \times (7 \times 16)$

_____

3. $15 \times 8 = 8 \times 15$

_____

4. $72 \times 1 = 72$

_____

Use properties of multiplication to find each product mentally. Show your steps and identify the properties that you used.

5. $76 \times 25 \times 4$

_____

_____

_____

_____

6. $5 \times 60 \times 20$

_____

_____

_____

_____

7. $40 \times 0 \times 17$

_____

_____

_____

8. $2 \times 4 \times 12$

_____

_____

_____

Spiral Review

Multiply. (Lesson 3–6)

9. $\begin{array}{r} 560 \\ \times\ 24 \\ \hline \end{array}$

10. $\begin{array}{r} 68 \\ \times\ 17 \\ \hline \end{array}$

11. $\begin{array}{r} 341 \\ \times\ 25 \\ \hline \end{array}$

12. $\begin{array}{r} 18 \\ \times\ 49 \\ \hline \end{array}$

13. $\begin{array}{r} 836 \\ \times\ 32 \\ \hline \end{array}$

14. $\begin{array}{r} 95 \\ \times\ 73 \\ \hline \end{array}$

15. $\begin{array}{r} 188 \\ \times\ 58 \\ \hline \end{array}$

16. $\begin{array}{r} 712 \\ \times\ 65 \\ \hline \end{array}$

3-7

Problem-Solving Practice
Multiplication Properties

Solve.

1. Eva needs to multiply 1 × 245. Give the product and name the property she would use.

   _____

2. Jose needs to multiply three numbers: (6 × 14) × 2. Give the product and name the property he would use.

   _____

Find the number that makes the sentence true.

3. Alicia uses the Commutative Property to find n.

   15 × 4 = *n* × 15

   _____

4. Peter uses the Associative Property to find n.

   (35 × 2) × 8 = 35 × (*n* × 8)

   _____

Solve.

5. During the summer, Henry read two books. The first book had 148 pages. The second book had twice as many pages. Henry's older brother read only one book, but it had twice as many pages as Henry's second book. Did Henry's brother read more or less than Henry?

   _____

6. The population of Delaware in the year 2000 was 783,600. The state has three counties: Kent, New Castle, and Sussex. Kent County has 126,697 people and New Castle has 500,265. Is the total population of Kent and New Castle counties more than four times the population of Sussex County?

   _____

Name _____ Date _____

Enrich

Multiplication Properties

Write two number sentences to show the Commutative Property of
Multiplication. Then shade the grids to show the number sentences
you wrote.

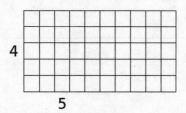   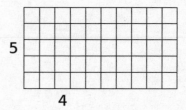

_____   _____

Write a number sentence to show the Identity Property of Multiplication.
Then shade the grid to show the number sentence you wrote.

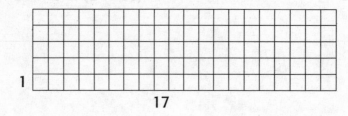

_____

Write a number sentence to show the Distributive Property. Then shade
the grid to show the number sentence you wrote.

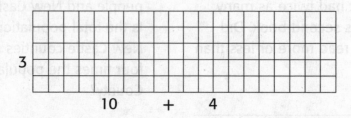

_____

Name _____ Date _____

Reteach

Extending Multiplication

Margaret would like to buy 4 notebooks that cost $3.08 a piece. The total cost will be 4 × $3.08. You can estimate the total cost using rounding.

4 × $3.08

4 × $3   Round $3.08 to $3 because $3.08 is closer to $3 than $4.

4 × $3 = $12   Multiply mentally.

So, the total cost of the notebooks is about $12.

Estimate each product.

1. $0.94 × 9	**2.** $3.92 × 5	**3.** $3.79 × 8
4. $2.82 × 4	**5.** $7.25 × 6	**6.** $2.67 × 2
7. $1.75 × 7	**8.** $68.70 × 4	**9.** $9.85 × 8
10. 20.1 × 9	**11.** 10.8 × 7	**12.** 79.3 × 40
13. 61.2 × 5	**14.** 23.4 × 60	**15.** 87.5 × 42

Name _____ Date _____

Skills Practice

Extending Multiplication

Estimate each product.

1. $1.80
   × 8

2. $2.83
   × 7

3. $14.75
   × 4

4. $31.15
   × 4

5. $4.80
   × 5

6. $1.67
   × 4

7. $1.79
   × 6

8. $2.26
   × 14

9. $9.72
   × 15

10. 8.4
    × 41

11. 48.2
    × 31

12. 14.7
    × 305

13. 42.3
    × 31

14. 104.6
    × 411

15. 21.3
    × 72

Solve.

16. Each Sunday during his nine week summer vacation, Ray buys a newspaper. The Sunday paper costs $1.85. About how much did Ray spend on the Sunday newspaper during his vacation?

_____

17. Jorge buys 8 pounds of ground beef for $3.29 a pound. About how much did he pay altogether?

_____

Name _____ Date _____

Homework Practice

Extending Multiplication

Estimate each product.

1. $5.27
    × 6

2. $3.36
    × 4

3. $12.17
    × 7

4. $4.28
    × 5

5. $8.17
    × 8

6. $1.32
    × 5

7. $27.64
    × 3

8. $63.44
    × 6

9. $17.55
    × 9

10. 7.7
    × 4

11. 11.9
    × 21

12. 51.7
    × 9

13. 33.3
    × 33

14. 87.2
    × 41

15. 17.6
    × 51

16. 27.1
    × 205

17. 72.1
    × 51

18. 92.1
    × 11

Spiral Review

Use properties of multiplication to find each product mentally. Show your steps and identify the properties that you used. (Lesson 3–7)

19. $5 × 14 × 2$

20. $50 × 6 × 20$

3-8

Problem-Solving Practice

Extending Multiplication

Solve.

1. Andrea earns $32.00 a day. After 9 days, about how much will she have earned?

   _____

2. Constantino bought 7 pounds of mozzarella cheese. Each pound costs $4.29. About how much did he spend altogether?

   _____

3. Kasi is traveling in the United States. If the exchange rate is 58 rupees for every American dollar, about how many rupees does it take to purchase a meal that costs $12.98?

   _____

4. A school receives $14.00 for every 1,000 labels they collect from certain products. About how much money will they make if students collect 3,000 labels?

   _____

5. In Spanish class, Kevin learns an average of 34 new words per month. If he takes Spanish for 3 years, about how many words will he learn?

   _____

6. An amusement park charges $35.50 for admission. On one day, 6,789 people visited the park. About how much money did the park make from admission that day?

   _____

Enrich

Extending Multiplication

Find each product to decode a secret message.

D	W	E	A
$5.70 × 34	$4.21 × 9	875 × 63	563 ×70
L	**U**	**I**	**Y**
$5.66 × 13	$7.19 × 34	89 × 876	123 × 342
P	**C**	**N**	**M**
$52.88 × 644	$32.99 × 211	65 × 65	$7.66 × 55
O	**H**	**S**	**G**
$12.44 × 555	2,233 × 155	$1.39 × 45	29 × 34
T	**I**	**O**	**T**
75 × 78	$45.85 × 25	$6.75 × 555	129 × 75

Match the letter in each box with one of the products below the lines. Write the letter on the line.

_____   _____   _____   _____
$37.89   77,964   5,850   346,115

___   ___   ___   ___   ___   ___   ___   ___
$193.80   55,125 $6,960.89 $1,146.25 $421.30   39,410 $73.58 $62.55

___   ___   ___   ___   ___   ___
42,066 $3,746.25 $244.46   986   55,125   5,850

___   ___   ___   ___   ___   ___   ___   ___
9,675   346,115   55,125 $34,054.72 $6,904.2   77,964   4,225   9,675

Name _____ Date _____

Reteach

Problem-Solving Investigation: Extra or Missing Information

Benjamin was in charge of selling tickets to the school play. On Monday he sold 10 tickets. He sold 8 tickets on Tuesday and again on Wednesday. On Thursday he sold 10 tickets, and on Friday he sold 5. The play was on Saturday at noon.

Find the amount of money Benjamin collected selling tickets to the school play.

Understand	**What facts do you know?** You know how many tickets Benjamin sold Monday–Friday. You also know when the play was. **What do you need to find?** How much money Benjamin collected selling tickets to the school play.
Plan	**Is there any information that is not needed?** The day and time of the play **Is there any information that is missing?** You do not know the cost of a ticket.
Solve	Since you do not have enough information, the problem cannot be solved.
Check	Read the question again to see if you missed any information. If so, go back and rework the problem. If not, the problem cannot be solved.

Solve each problem. If there is extra information, identify it. If there is not enough information, tell what information is needed.

1. Julia drinks 5 glasses of water on day 1 and 4 glasses of water on day 2. She also drank 4 glasses of water on day 3. She drank 7 glasses on day 4. She also had some juice on day 4. What is the total number of glasses of water she drank at the end of the four days.

_____

48

Reteach

Problem-Solving Investigation: Extra or Missing Information   (continued)

Solve each problem. If there is extra information, identify it. If there is not enough information, tell what information is needed.

2. Susan bikes 3 miles round-trip from home to school, Monday through Friday. On Saturday and Sunday she does not ride her bike, but skateboards around her neighborhood. How many miles total does she bike to and from school each week?

_____

3. Jason's goal is to wash 30 cars on the day of his scout troop's car wash fundraiser. If he washes 5 cars between 9:00 and 11:00 A.M. and 10 more cars between noon and 2:30, will he meet his goal?

_____

4. Carl is planting an herb garden. If his garden has 3 rows and he can plant three herbs in each row, how many herbs can he grow?

_____

5. Mr. Davis has too much stuff so he is having a yard sale. He wants to make at least $200 from the sale. If he has sold $20 worth of his belongings to five different people, has he reached his goal?

_____

6. Marissa can run 1 mile in 10 minutes. How many miles will she run in a half hour?

_____

7. Zach really enjoys listening to music. If Zach listens to 3 hours of music a day, how many total hours of music will he listen to in 7 days?

_____

3-9

Skills Practice

Problem-Solving Investigation: Extra or Missing Information

Solve each problem. If there is extra information, identify it. If there is not enough information, tell what information is needed.

1. Mrs. Blackwell gives each of her students two pencils. How many pencils did she hand out?

   _____

2. Mary has saved $50. If she wants to buy an mp3 player that costs $250, will she have enough money in six months?

   _____

3. Marco does 10 extra math problems each school night. How many extra problems does he do each school week?

   _____

4. Juan's family is from Houston. They want to go to Florida for vacation. If they need $100 for each person in the family in order to be able to make the trip, will they have enough?

   _____

5. Shannon has five red shirts, three blue shirts, and four purple shirts. She has three more white shirts than she does brown shirts. How many brown shirts does she have?

   _____

6. If David plays 3 tennis matches every week for 9 weeks, how many matches will he play altogether?

   _____

Name _____ Date _____

Homework Practice

Problem-Solving Investigation

Solve each problem. If there is extra information, identify it. If there is not enough information, tell what information is needed.

1. The Alvarez family bought a car for $2,000. They made a down payment of $500. If they want to pay the balance in five equal payments, how much will each of these payments be?

   _____

2. Melanie can walk five miles in a half hour. How many miles will she walk in one week?

   _____

3. Jamie and Melissa both have 30 CDs. How many more CDs does John have?

   _____

4. Anna collected 50 cans for a food drive. She collected 10 cans each day of the drive, mostly green beans. How many days did she collect cans?

   _____

Spiral Review

Estimate.

5. $6.82
    × 4

6. $3.37
    × 2

7. $41.64
    × 12

8. $35.61
    × 24

9. $17.52
    × 18

10. 2.67
    × 54

11. 94.2
    × 76

12. 76.4
    × 127

13. 8.6
    × 82

51

Enrich
Extra or Missing Information

Use the chart to solve the problems. If there is not enough information to solve, write *not enough information* and tell what information is needed. If you can estimate the missing information, write *estimate*, and explain your estimate. If there is too much information, write *too much information* and tell what information you need to solve the problem.

Sports Caps	
Color	**Number of Students**
Red	4
Blue	12
Black	16
White	8

Rebecca's school will order sports caps with the school name. She is taking color requests from her classmates. She has 40 requests so far.

1. Rebecca plans to take 10 more requests. What fraction of the requests did she already have for red caps?

_____

_____

2. Rebecca just added 8 more requests. Now what fraction of the total requests are for black caps?

_____

_____

3. If Rebecca takes 50 requests, how many will be for white caps?

_____

_____

4. The blue and the red caps costs $1.50 more than the black and the white caps. What is the total cost of the blue caps requested?

_____

_____

5. The blue caps cost $5.50 each and the black caps cost $4.00 each. What is the total cost of the black caps requested so far?

_____

Name _____ Date _____

Individual Progress Checklist

Learning Mastery			Lesson	Lesson Goal	Comments
B	D	M			
			3-1	Use basic facts and patterns to multiply multiples of 10, 100, and 1,000 mentally.	
			3-2	Use the Distributive Property to multiply mentally.	
			3-3	Estimate products by rounding and using the clustering strategy.	
			3-4	Multiply up to a three-digit number by a one-digit number.	
			3-5	Solve problems by drawing a picture.	
			3-6	Multiply up to a three-digit number by a two-digit number.	
			3-7	Use the associative and commutative properties to multiply mentally.	
			3-8	Multiply to solve problems involving money and greater numbers.	
			3-9	Identify extra information or missing information to solve a problem.	

B = Beginning; **D** = Developing; **M** = Mastered

Note to Parents

_____

_____

_____

_____

_____

Name _____ Date _____

Chapter Diagnostic Test

Multiply.

1. 9×4

2. 3×10

3. 5×5

4. 6×8

5. 1×4

6. 7×9

7. The length of a pencil is 7 inches. Find the total length of 4 pencils placed end to end.

Write a multiplication problem for each. Then find each product.

8. 5 people each have 8 toy cars

9. 6 dolls at $6 each

10. 2 boxes of 8 crayons

11. There are 7 students sitting at each table in the cafeteria. How many students are sitting at 8 tables?

Add.

12. $\begin{array}{r} 4{,}238 \\ + 31{,}169 \end{array}$

13. $\begin{array}{r} 173 \\ + 2{,}416 \end{array}$

14. $\begin{array}{r} 914 \\ + 14{,}134 \end{array}$

15. Sal's Italian Café sold 5,345 sandwiches last month. This month, they sold 173 more sandwiches than last month. Next month, they hope to sell 250 more sandwiches than they sold this month. How many sandwiches does Sal's hope to sell next month?

1. _____

2. _____

3. _____

4. _____

5. _____

6. _____

7. _____

8. _____

9. _____

10. _____

11. _____

12. _____

13. _____

14. _____

15. _____

3

Chapter Pretest

Find each product mentally.

1. 8 × 50

2. 330 × 100

Rewrite each expression using the Distributive Property. Then evaluate.

3. 3 × (40 + 4)

4. 7 × (20 + 8)

Estimate by rounding. Show your work.

5. 33 × 17

6. 107 × 41

Estimate. Then multiply.

7. 27 × 3

8. 42 × 14

9. 108 × 8

10. 103 × 52

Identify the multiplication property used to rewrite each problem.

11. 145 × 1 = 145

12. 2 × 3 × 5 = 3 × 5 × 2

Estimate.

13. $5.62
  ×   3

14.   62.6
  ×   39

Solve the problem. If there is extra information, identify it. If there is not enough information, tell what information is needed.

15. Carla mixed enough cookie dough to make 3 dozen cookies for her friend's birthday party. How many cookies will each party guest receive?

1. _____

2. _____

3. _____

4. _____

5. _____

6. _____

7. _____

8. _____

9. _____

10. _____

11. _____

12. _____

13. _____

14. _____

15. _____

Assessment

Name _____ Date _____

Quiz 1 *(Lessons 3–1 through 3–3)*

Find each product mentally.

1. 4 × 60

2. 80 × 800

3. At a swimming championship, there were 20 teams competing. If each team has 14 members, how many swimmers were at the championship?

Rewrite each expression using the Distributive Property. Show the steps that you used.

4. 2 × 54

5. 67 × 4

Estimate by rounding. Show your work.

6. 68
   ×45

7. 408
   × 34

Estimate by clustering. Show your work.

8. Elsa buys a bag of oranges for $2.95, a bag of apples for $3.03, a carton of strawberries for $3.15, and a pint of blackberries for $2.99. About how much did she spend?

1. _____

2. _____

3. _____

4. _____

5. _____

6. _____

7. _____

8. _____

Name _____ Date _____

Quiz 2 *(Lessons 3–4 through 3–6)*

Multiply.

1. 7 × 53

2. 3 × 631

3. The baby gorilla at the zoo weighs 6 pounds. The baby elephant at the zoo weighs 34 times as much. How much does the baby elephant weigh?

Solve.

4. Liam's display shelf is 63 inches wide. If he puts 7 bowling trophies on the shelf, and each trophy is 4 inches wide, how many cross-country awards can he also fit on the shelf if each award is 6 inches wide? How much space remains on the shelf?

Multiply.

5. 36
   ×37

6. 241
   × 51

7. Matilda earns $11 an hour for babysitting. How much will she earn in 3 weeks if she babysits 15 hours each week?

1. _____

2. _____

3. _____

4. _____

5. _____

6. _____

7. _____

Identify the multiplication property used to rewrite each problem.

1. $12 \times (5 \times 7) = (12 \times 5) \times 7$

2. $71 \times 43 \times 95 = 43 \times 95 \times 71$

Estimate.

3. $\begin{array}{r} \$4.79 \\ \times\ \ 16 \\ \hline \end{array}$ 4. $\begin{array}{r} \$11.62 \\ \times\ \ 7 \\ \hline \end{array}$ 5. $\begin{array}{r} 6.1 \\ \times\ 12 \\ \hline \end{array}$

6. Grapefruits cost $2.49 per pound. If Jenny bought 7 pounds of grapefruit at the farmer's market this morning, how much did they cost?

Solve each problem. If there is extra information, identify it. If there is not enough information, tell what information is needed.

7. Mark is bringing 3 friends with him to tonight's concert. His parents bought 15 tickets to the concert. If each ticket costs $14 dollars, how much did Mark's parents spend?

8. Grace completed practice math problems for 1.5 hours a day every day this week. How many total problems did she complete?

1. _____

2. _____

3. _____

4. _____

5. _____

6. _____

7. _____

8. _____

Name _____ Date _____

Mid-Chapter Test (Lessons 3–1 through 3–4)

Find each product mentally.

1. 7 × 40

2. 60 × 2,000

Rewrite each expression using the Distributive Property. Show the steps that you used.

3. 3 × 72

4. 94 × 6

Estimate by rounding. Show your work.

5. 18 × 92

6. The following table shows the number of badges earned by four Girl Scout troops in the Houston area. Use clustering to estimate the total number of badges earned.

Troop	Badges Earned
1	502
2	496
3	513
4	487

Multiply.

7. 67 × 3

8. 8 × 214

1. _____

2. _____

3. _____

4. _____

5. _____

6. _____

7. _____

8. _____

Assessment

Vocabulary Test

Match each word to its definition. Write your answers on the lines provided.

1. cluster _____	**A.** The answer to a multiplication problem.
2. Distributive Property _____	**B.** group together
3. factor _____	**C.** The property which states that the grouping of the factors does not change the product.
4. product _____	**D.** The property that states that to multiply a sum by a number, you can multiply each addend by the same number and add the products.
5. Associative Property _____	**E.** A number that divides into a whole number evenly. Also, a number that is multiplied by another number.

Name _____ Date _____

Oral Assessment

For this activity, gather a box of 100 paper clips or a similar number of other small objects and model for the student the concept of arranging the objects into smaller groups and using the Distributive Property to aid with mental multiplication.

Read each question aloud to the student. The student should rearrange the objects into smaller groups. Then write the student's answers on the lines below the question.

1. If you want to multiply 6×16, how many groups of 6 objects should you make?

_____

2. How can you separate 16 into two numbers that are easier to multiply by 6? What two groups of objects do you now have?

_____

3. What is 6×10?

_____

4. What is 6×6

_____

5. What is $60 + 36$?

_____

6. Write the original problem using the Distributive Property.

_____

Assessment

Name _____ Date _____

Oral Assessment (continued)

For the word problem that follows, the student will need to draw a square that is 12 in. × 12 in. on a piece of paper and divide the square horizontally into 1-in. increments. Work through the word problem with the student by reading each question aloud and writing the student's answer on the lines that follow.

Farmer McAllister has a plot of land that is 12 feet long by 12 feet wide. He wants to plant 3 rows of lettuce, 4 rows of tomatoes, and 2 rows of beans. Each row of vegetables is 1 foot wide and 12 feet long, and in between each crop, he must leave 1 foot of empty soil. Does he have enough room in his plot of land to plant all the rows of vegetables he desires?

7. What facts do you know about the plot of land?

_____

8. Look at the square on the paper in front of you. How many rows do you see?

_____

9. How many total rows of space will the vegetables need to grow?

_____

10. How many total rows of empty soil will he need?

_____

11. If you add up the empty rows and the rows of vegetables, does Farmer McAllister have enough room on his plot of land?

_____

Chapter Project Rubric

Score	Explanation
3	Student successfully completed the chapter project. Student demonstrated appropriate use of chapter information in completing the chapter project.
2	Student completed the chapter project with partial success. Student partially demonstrated appropriate use of chapter information in completing the chapter project.
1	Student completed the chapter project with little success. Student demonstrated very little appropriate use of chapter information in completing the chapter project.
0	Student did not complete the chapter project. Student demonstrated inappropriate use of chapter information in completing the chapter project.

Assessment

Foldables® Rubric

Multiply Whole Numbers

Layered look Foldable

Score	Explanation
3	Student properly assembled Foldables® graphic organizer according to instructions. Student recorded information related to the chapter in the manner directed by the Foldables graphic organizer. Student used the Foldables graphic organizer as a study guide and organizational tool.
2	Student exhibited partial understanding of proper Foldables graphic organizer assembly. Student recorded most but not all information related to the chapter in the manner directed by the Foldables graphic organizer. Student demonstrated partial use of the Foldables graphic organizer as a study guide and organizational tool.
1	Student showed little understanding of proper Foldables graphic organizer assembly. Student recorded only some information related to the chapter in the manner directed by the Foldables graphic organizer. Student demonstrated little use of the Foldables graphic organizer as a study guide and organizational tool.
0	Student did not assemble Foldables graphic organizer according to instructions. Student recorded little or no information related to the chapter in the manner directed by the Foldables graphic organizer. Student did not use the Foldables graphic organizer as a study guide and organizational tool.

Name _____ Date _____

Chapter Test, Form 1

Read each question carefully. Write your answer on the line provided.

1. Find the product mentally. 50×70

   A. 35   **B.** 350   **C.** 3,500   **D.** 35,000   1. _____

2. Find the missing factor.

   $6 \times$ _____ $= 48,000$

   F. 8,000   **G.** 800   **H.** 80   **J.** 8   2. _____

3. Find the product mentally. 3×15

   A. 60   **B.** 55   **C.** 50   **D.** 45   3. _____

4. Find the product mentally. 4×17

   F. 62   **G.** 64   **H.** 66   **J.** 68   4. _____

5. Mr. Lee is buying 5 movie tickets for $12 each. What is the total cost of the tickets?

   A. $50   **B.** $55   **C.** $60   **D.** $65   5. _____

6. Walter reads 37 pages each week. How many pages does he read in 8 weeks?

   F. 296   **G.** 269   **H.** 246   **J.** 249   6. _____

7. Estimate by rounding. 6×34

   A. 204   **B.** 200   **C.** 180   **D.** 175   7. _____

8. A hotel charges $300 per room per week. How much did the hotel make if they rented 70 rooms for one week?

   F. $210,000   **G.** $21,000   **H.** $2,100   **J.** $210   8. _____

9. Find the product. 149×3

   A. 563   **B.** 447   **C.** 341   **D.** 299   9. _____

10. Farview Elementary purchased 8 new computer systems for the computer lab. Each system cost $1,398. What was the total cost?

    F. $13,599   **G.** $ 12,228   **H.** $11,184   **J.** $10,398   10. _____

11. Find the product. 19×16

    A. 285   **B.** 288   **C.** 304   **D.** 320   11. _____

Chapter Test, Form 1   (continued)

12. Janie arranged chairs for a presentation. Each row contained 14
    chairs and she arranged 22 rows. How many chairs were arranged?
    F. 322   **G.** 308   **H.** 294   **J.** 140   12. _____

13. Find the number that makes the sentence true.
    $3 \times 15 \times 9 = 9 \times 3 \times$ _____
    A. 9   **B.** 3   **C.** 15   **D.** 405   13. _____

14. Find the number that makes the sentence true.
    $(28 \times 31) \times 8 = 31 \times (28 \times$ _____$)$ 14. _____
    F. 28   **G.** 31   **H.** 8   **J.** 9

15. A school has 17 classrooms with 25 student desks in each
    classroom. How many student desks are in the school?   15. _____
    A. 375   **B.** 400   **C.** 425   **D.** 450

16. Estimate. $1.30 × 5
    F. $5.00   **G.** $56.00   **H.** $65.00   **J.** $650   16. _____

17. Estimate. 3.1 × 52
    A. 15   **B.** 150   **C.** 1,500   **D.** 15,000   17. _____

18. Mr. Gray bought 21 boxes of crayons for his students. Each box
    contained 12 crayons. How many crayons did Mr. Gray buy?
    F. 144   **G.** 212   **H.** 252   **J.** 292   18. _____

19. Kerry is collecting money for charity. Her goal is to collect $100.
    She has collected $15 each from 6 people so far. How much more   19. _____
    money does she need to collect to reach her goal?
    A. $90   **B.** $10   **C.** $5   **D.** $1

20. Sean has 11 cartoon DVDs, 3 action DVDs, and 9 adventure DVDs.   20. _____
    How many DVDs does Sean have that are not action or adventure?
    F. 3   **G.** 9   **H.** 11   **J.** 23

Chapter Test, Form 2A

Read each question carefully. Write your answer on the line provided.

1. Find the product mentally. 40×60
   A. 24   **B.** 240   **C.** 2,400   **D.** 24,000

   1. _____

2. Find the missing factor.

   $8 \times$ _____ $= 48,000$
   F. 6,000   **G.** 600   **H.** 60   **J.** 6

   2. _____

3. Find the product mentally. 4×18
   A. 72   **B.** 55   **C.** 50   **D.** 45

   3. _____

4. Find the product mentally. 3×14
   F. 42   **G.** 44   **H.** 46   **J.** 48

   4. _____

5. Mr. Lee is buying 6 movie tickets for $13 each. What is the total cost of the tickets?
   A. $70   **B.** $72   **C.** $78   **D.** $80

   5. _____

6. Walter reads 32 pages each week. How many pages does he read in 9 weeks?
   F. 296   **G.** 288   **H.** 246   **J.** 249

   6. _____

7. Estimate by rounding. 6×22
   A. 132   **B.** 122   **C.** 120   **D.** 115

   7. _____

8. A hotel charges $400 per room per week. How much did the hotel make if they rented 80 rooms for one week?
   F. $320,000   **G.** $32,000   **H.** $3,200   **J.** $320

   8. _____

9. Find the product. 164×3
   A. 563   **B.** 492   **C.** 341   **D.** 299

   9. _____

10. Farview Elementary purchased 7 new computer systems for the computer lab. Each system cost $1,298. What was the total cost?
    F. $10,876   **G.** $9,903   **H.** $9,086   **J.** $8,765

    10. _____

11. Find the product. 17×11
    A. 135   **B.** 187   **C.** 204   **D.** 220

    11. _____

Chapter Test, Form 2A   *(continued)*

12. Janie arranged chairs for a presentation. Each row contained 12 chairs and she arranged 18 rows. How many chairs were arranged?

    F. 222   **G.** 218   **H.** 216   **J.** 140

    12. _____

13. Find the number that makes the sentence true.

    $1 \times 14 \times 9 = 9 \times 1 \times$ _____

    A. 9   **B.** 1   **C.** 14   **D.** 126

    13. _____

14. Find the number that makes the sentence true.

    $(22 \times 17) \times 8 = 17 \times (22 \times$ _____ $)$

    F. 22   **G.** 17   **H.** 8   **J.** 9

    14. _____

15. A school has 14 classrooms with 28 student desks in each classroom. How many student desks are in the school?

    A. 392   **B.** 400   **C.** 425   **D.** 450

    15. _____

16. Estimate. 1.70×8

    F. \$8   **G.** \$16   **H.** \$160   **J.** \$1,600

    16. _____

17. Estimate. 2.3×52

    A. 10   **B.** 100   **C.** 1,000   **D.** 10,000

    17. _____

18. Mr. Gray bought 26 boxes of crayons. Each box contained 12 crayons. How many crayons did Mr. Gray buy?

    F. 144   **G.** 212   **H.** 252   **J.** 312

    18. _____

19. Kerry is collecting money for school. Her goal is to get \$200. She has collected \$15 each from 12 people so far. How much more money does she need to reach her goal?

    A. \$180   **B.** \$20   **C.** \$15   **D.** \$10

    19. _____

20. Sean has 13 cartoon DVDs, 4 action DVDs, and 8 adventure DVDs. How many DVDs does Sean have that are not action or adventure?

    F. 3   **G.** 12   **H.** 13   **J.** 25

    20. _____

Name _____ Date _____

Chapter Test, Form 2B

Read each question carefully. Write your answer on the line provided.

1. Solve mentally. 40 × 60
   A. 24   **B.** 240   **C.** 2,400

   1. _____

2. Find the missing number.

   8 × _____ = 48,000
   F. 6,000   **G.** 600   **H.** 60

   2. _____

3. Solve mentally. 4 × 18
   A. 72   **B.** 55   **C.** 50

   3. _____

4. Solve mentally. 3 × 14
   F. 42   **G.** 44   **H.** 46

   4. _____

5. Mr. Lee buys 6 movie tickets for 13 dollars each. What is the total?
   A. 70   **B.** 72   **C.** 78

   5. _____

6. Walter reads 32 pages each week. How many pages does he read in 9 weeks?
   F. 296   **G.** 288   **H.** 246

   6. _____

7. Estimate by rounding. 6 × 22
   A. 132   **B.** 122   **C.** 120

   7. _____

8. A hotel costs $400 per room per week. How much does the hotel make if they rent 80 rooms for one week?
   F. $320,000   **G.** $32,000   **H.** $3,200

   8. _____

9. Find the product. 164 × 3
   A. 563   **B.** 492   **C.** 341

   9. _____

10. Farview Elementary bought 7 new computer systems. Each cost $1,298. What was the total cost?
    F. $10,876   **G.** $9,903   **H.** $9,086

    10. _____

11. Find the product. 17 × 11
    A. 135   **B.** 187   **C.** 204

    11. _____

Assessment

Name _____ Date _____

Chapter Test, Form 2B *(continued)*

12. Janie arranged chairs in rows. Each row had 12 chairs and she arranged 18 rows. How many chairs were arranged?

F. 222   **G.** 218   **H.** 216   12. _____

13. What number makes the sentence true.

$1 \times 14 \times 9 = 9 \times 1 \times$ _____

A. 9   **B.** 1   **C.** 14   13. _____

14. What number makes the sentence true.

$(22 \times 17) \times 8 = 17 \times (22 \times$ _____$)$

F. 22   **G.** 17   **H.** 8   14. _____

15. A school has 14 rooms with 28 desks in each room. How many desks are in the school?

A. 392   **B.** 400   **C.** 425   15. _____

16. Estimate. $\$1.70 \times 8$

F. $8   **G.** $16   **H.** $160   16. _____

17. Estimate. 2.3×52

A. 10   **B.** 100   **C.** 1,000   17. _____

18. Mr. Gray bought 26 boxes of crayons. Each box contained 12 crayons. How many crayons did Mr. Gray buy?

F. 212   **G.** 252   **H.** 312   18. _____

19. Kerry is collecting money for school. Her goal is to get $200. She has collected $15 each from 12 people so far. How much more money does she need to reach her goal?

A. $180   **B.** $20   **C.** $15   19. _____

20. Sean has 13 cartoon DVDs, 4 funny DVDs, and 8 sad DVDs. How many DVDs does Sean have that are not funny or sad?

F. 3   **G.** 12   **H.** 13   20. _____

Name _____ Date _____

Chapter Test, Form 2C

Copyright © Macmillan/McGraw-Hill, a division of The McGraw-Hill Companies, Inc.

Read each question carefully. Write your answer on the line provided.

1. Find the product mentally. 40×60

    1. _____

2. Find the missing factor.
   $8 \times$ _____ $= 48,000$

    2. _____

3. Find the product mentally. 4×18

    3. _____

4. Find the product mentally. 3×14

    4. _____

5. Mr. Lee is buying 6 movie tickets for 13 dollars each. What is the total cost of the tickets?

    5. _____

6. Walter reads 32 pages each week. How many pages does he read in 9 weeks?

    6. _____

7. Estimate by rounding. 6×22

    7. _____

8. A hotel charges $400 per room per week. How much did the hotel make if they rented 80 rooms for one week?

    8. _____

9. Find the product. 164×3

    9. _____

10. Farview Elementary purchased 7 new computer systems for the computer lab. Each system cost $1,298. What was the total cost?

    10. _____

11. Find the product. 17×11

    11. _____

12. Janie arranged chairs for a presentation. Each row contained 12 chairs and she arranged 18 rows. How many chairs were arranged?

    12. _____

13. Find the number that makes the sentence true.
    $1 \times 14 \times 9 = 9 \times 1 \times$ _____

    13. _____

Name _____ Date _____

Chapter Test, Form 2C *(continued)*

14. Find the number that makes the sentence true.

(22 × 17) × 8 = 17 × (22 × _____)

14. _____

15. A school has 14 classrooms with 28 student desks in each classroom. How many student desks are in the school?

15. _____

16. Estimate. $1.70 × 8

16. _____

17. Estimate. 2.3 × 52

17. _____

18. Mr. Gray bought 26 boxes of crayons for his students. Each box contained 12 crayons. How many crayons did Mr. Gray buy?

18. _____

19. Kerry is collecting money for charity. Her goal is to collect $200. She has collected $15 each from 12 people so far. How much more money does she need to collect to reach her goal?

19. _____

20. Sean has 13 cartoon DVDs, 4 action DVDs, and 8 adventure DVDs. How many DVDs does Sean have that are not action or adventure?

20. _____

Chapter Test, Form 2D

Read each question carefully. Write your answer on the line provided.

1. Solve mentally. 40×60

   1. _____

2. Find the missing factor.
   $8 \times$ _____ $= 48,000$

   2. _____

3. Solve mentally. 4×18

   3. _____

4. Solve mentally. 3×14

   4. _____

5. Mr. Lee buys 6 movie tickets for 13 dollars each. What is the cost of the tickets?

   5. _____

6. Walter reads 32 pages each week. How many pages does he read in 9 weeks?

   6. _____

7. Round then multiply. 6×22

   7. _____

8. A hotel costs $400 per room per week. How much does the hotel make if they rented 80 rooms for one week?

   8. _____

9. Find the product. 164×3

   9. _____

10. Farview Elementary bought 7 new computer systems. Each cost $1,298. What was the total cost?

    10. _____

11. Find the product. 17×11

    11. _____

12. Janie set up chairs for a presentation. Each row contained 12 chairs and she set up 18 rows. How many chairs were set up?

    12. _____

13. What number makes the sentence true?
    $1 \times 14 \times 9 = 9 \times 1 \times$ _____

    13. _____

14. Find the number that makes the sentence true.
(22 × 17) × 8 = 17 × (22 × _____)

14. _____

15. A school has 14 rooms with 28 desks in each. How many desks are in the school?

15. _____

16. Estimate. $1.70 × 8

16. _____

17. Estimate. 2.3 × 52

17. _____

18. Mr. Gray bought 26 boxes of crayons. Each box had 12 crayons. How many crayons did Mr. Gray buy?

18. _____

19. Kerry is collecting money for school. Her goal is to collect $200. She has collected $15 each from 12 people so far. How much more money does she need to collect to reach her goal?

19. _____

20. Sean has 13 cartoon DVDs, 4 sad DVDs, and 8 funny DVDs. How many DVDs does Sean have that are not sad or funny?

20. _____

Name _____ Date _____

Chapter Test, Form 3

Read each question carefully. Write your answer on the line provided.

1. Find the product mentally. 400 × 60

    1. _____

2. Find the missing factor.

    12 × _____ = 72,000

    2. _____

3. Find the product mentally. 4 × 19

    3. _____

4. Find the product mentally. 3 × 27

    4. _____

5. Mr. Lee is buying 6 movie tickets for $13.50 each. What is the total cost of the tickets?

    5. _____

6. Walter reads 132 pages each week. How many pages does he read in 9 weeks?

    6. _____

7. Estimate by rounding. 6 × 22

    7. _____

8. A hotel charges $430 per room per week. How much did the hotel make if they rented 80 rooms for one week?

    8. _____

9. Find the product. 164 × 3

    9. _____

10. Farview Elementary purchased 17 new computer systems for the computer lab. Each system cost $1,298. What was the total cost?

    10. _____

11. Find the product. 17 × 11

    11. _____

12. Janie arranged chairs for a presentation. Each row contained 12 chairs and she arranged 22 rows. How many chairs were arranged?

    12. _____

13. Find the number that makes the sentence true.

    1 × 14 × 9 = 9 × 1 × _____

    13. _____

14. Find the number that makes the sentence true.
$(22 \times 17) \times 8 = 17 \times (22 \times \underline{\hspace{1cm}})$

14. _____

15. A school has 18 classrooms with 27 student desks in each classroom. How many student desks are in the school?

15. _____

16. Estimate. 1.70×8

16. _____

17. Estimate. 2.3×52

17. _____

18. Mr. Gray bought 26 boxes of crayons for his students. Each box contained 13 crayons. How many crayons did Mr. Gray buy?

18. _____

19. Kerry is collecting money for charity. Her goal is to collect $200. She has collected $15 each from 12 people so far. How much more money does she need to collect to reach her goal?

19. _____

20. Sean has 13 cartoon DVDs, 4 action DVDs, and 8 adventure DVDs. How many DVDs does Sean have that are not action or adventure?

20. _____

Name _____ Date _____

Chapter Extended-Response Test

Demonstrate your knowledge by giving a clear, concise solution to each problem. Be sure to include all relevant drawings and justify your answers. You may show your solution in more than one way or investigate beyond the requirements of the problem. If necessary, record your answer on another piece of paper.

1. Explain two different ways that you could use mental math and multiplication properties to find 50 × 6,000 × 2. Show your steps and identify the properties you used.

2. The price of admission to the science museum is $12. The museum needs to make $36,000 in August. The museum has already made $18,720.

   a. How many tickets has the museum already sold?

   b. How much more money does the museum need to meet its goal?

   c. How many more tickets need to be sold?

Name _____ Date _____

Cumulative Test Practice Chapters 1–3

Test Example

There are 48 rows in the school auditorium. Each row can seat 12 people. If every row is full, how many people can be seated in the auditorium at the same time?

A. 480   **B.** 523   **C.** 576   **D.** 765

Read the Item

To find the total number of people in the auditorium, you need to find the product of 48 and 12.

Solve the Item

Multiply 48 by 12.

$$
\begin{array}{r}
48 \\
\times\ 12 \\
\hline
96 \\
+\ 48 \\
\hline
576
\end{array}
$$

The number of people in the cafeteria is 576.

The answer is C.

1. A souvenir shop has 41 boxes of cards in stock. Each box contains 9 cards. Use rounding to estimate the total number of cards.

   A. 380   **B.** 400   **C.** 410   **D.** 450   1. _____

2. Jorge bought a pack of gum for $0.89. He received $0.11 in change. What is the least number of coins he could have received?

   F. 2   **G.** 3   **H.** 4   **J.** 5   2. _____

3. There are 22 students in a classroom. Each student has 5 pencils. How many pencils are there altogether?

   A. 105   **B.** 110   **C.** 125   **D.** 140   3. _____

Cumulative Test Practice *(continued)*

4. Jenny has 270 cards in her collection. She has 60 cards more than Ricky and 25 cards fewer than Sara. How many cards does Sara have?

  F. 210

  G. 225

  H. 275

  J. 295

4. _____

5. How much smaller is California than Texas?

California	163,707 sq mi
Texas	268,601 sq mi

  A. 96,272 sq mi

  B. 104,894 sq mi

  C. 106,302 sq mi

  D. 112,584 sq mi

5. _____

6. The distance from Earth to the sun is about 93,000,000 miles. How is this number written in words?

  F. ninety-three thousand

  G. ninety-three hundred thousand

  H. ninety-three million

  J. ninety-three billion

6. _____

7. Mrs. Kelly has 28 boxes of crayons in her classroom. If each box has 4 crayons, how many crayons are there?

  A. 112   **C.** 118

  B. 116   **D.** 124

7. _____

8. The auditorium has 62 rows with 12 seats each. If 320 seats are occupied, which of the following ways shows how to find the number of empty seats?

  F. Add 320 to the product of 62 and 12.

  G. Add 42 to the product of 62 and 12.

  H. Subtract 320 from the product of 62 and 12.

  J. Subtract 62 from the product of 320 and 12.

8. _____

9. A car dealer has 59 cars on its lot. Each car has 4 wheels. How many wheels are there altogether at the car dealer?

   A. 184

   B. 208

   C. 216

   D. 236

   9. _____

10. The price of gas over the past 4 weeks is shown in the table. If the pattern continues, what will the price be after 5 weeks?

Week	1	2	3	4	5
Price($)	1.00	1.80	2.60	3.40	?

   F. $4.00

   G. $4.10

   H. $4.15

   J. $4.20

   10. _____

11. Betty runs 4 miles every week. How many miles does she run in 16 weeks?

   11. _____

12. A bookshelf holds 23 books on each shelf. There are 12 shelves. How many books are there on the bookshelf?

   12. _____

13. There are 3 kids in the Smith family. If each child has 28 teeth, how many teeth do the Smith kids have altogether?

   13. _____

14. Mary and Rob each have two bags with 6 pencils in each. How many pencils do they have altogether?

   14. _____

15. There are 13 girls in the 5th grade. Each girls has two barrettes in her hair. How many barrettes are in the class?

   15. _____

Name _____ Date _____

Student Recording Sheet

Use this recording sheet with pages 144–145 of the Student Edition.

Read each question. Then fill in the correct answer.

1. Ⓐ Ⓑ Ⓒ Ⓓ   10. _____

2. Ⓕ Ⓖ Ⓗ Ⓙ   11. _____

3. Ⓐ Ⓑ Ⓒ Ⓓ   12. _____

4. Ⓕ Ⓖ Ⓗ Ⓙ   _____

                                          _____

5. Ⓐ Ⓑ Ⓒ Ⓓ

6. Ⓕ Ⓖ Ⓗ Ⓙ

7. Ⓐ Ⓑ Ⓒ Ⓓ

8. Ⓕ Ⓖ Ⓗ Ⓙ

9. Ⓐ Ⓑ Ⓒ Ⓓ

Assessment

Answers (Graphic Organizer and Anticipation Guide)

Anticipation Guide

Name _____ **Date** _____

3 Anticipation Guide

Multiply Whole Numbers

STEP 1 *Before you begin Chapter 3*

- Read each statement.
- Decide whether you agree (A) or disagree (D) with the statement.
- Write A or D in the first column OR if you are not sure whether you agree or disagree, write NS (not sure).

STEP 1 A, D, or NS	Statement	STEP 2 A or D
	1. The Distributive Property combines multiplication and addition.	A
	2. The product is the result of two or more numbers that are multiplied.	A
	3. The Identity Property is the product of any factor and 1.	A
	4. This is an example of the Commutative Property: $4 \times 5 + 8 = 4 \times 8 + 5$	D
	5. The Associative Property states that the order of the factors does not change the product.	A
	6. $6 \times 3 = 18$ is an example of the Distributive Property.	D

STEP 2 *After you complete Chapter 3*

- Reread each statement and complete the last column by entering an A (agree) or a D (disagree).
- Did any of your opinions about the statements change from the first column?
- For those statements that you mark with a D, use a separate sheet of paper to explain why you disagree. Use examples, if possible.

Name _____ **Date** _____

3 Graphic Organizer

Use this graphic organizer to take notes on **Chapter 3: Multiply Whole Numbers.** Fill in the missing information.

Distributive Property	$6 \times (3 + 5) = 6 \times 8$ **or 48** $(6 \times 3) + (6 \times 5) = 18 +$ **30 or 48** The Distributive Property combines **addition** and **multiplication**.
Factor	$2 \times \underline{4} = 8$ The numbers that are multiplied are factors of the **product**.
Product	$3 \times 3 = \underline{9}$ $4 \times 5 = \underline{20}$ The **result** when two or more numbers are multiplied.
Clustering	$523 + 499 + 506 =$ $500 + 500 + 500 = 1,500$ So, $523 + 499 + 506$ is **about 1,500.** Each of the three numbers is close to **500** , so think $3 \times 5 = 15$ and add two zeroes.

Chapter Resources

Answers

3–1 Reteach
Name _____ Date _____

Multiplication Patterns

To multiply by multiples of 10, 100, and 1,000, you can use basic facts and patterns.

Multiply 40 × 800.

Start with the basic fact. $4 \times 8 = 32$

Count the number of zeros in each factor and add them together. 40×800

Write that number of zeros in the product. 1 zero + 2 zeros = 3 zeros $40 \times 800 = 32,000$

Multiply 50 × 80.

Start with the basic fact. $5 \times 8 = 40$

Count the number of zeros in each factor and add them together. 50×80

Write that number of zeros in the product. 1 zero + 1 zero = 2 zeros $50 \times 80 = 4,000$

Complete.

1. 20 × 60

   Basic fact: $2 \times 6 = $ **12**

   Number of zeros in each factor: **1** + **1** = **2**

   Product: $20 \times 60 = $ **1,200**

2. 9 × 80

   Basic fact: $9 \times 8 = $ **72**

   Number of zeros in each factor: **0** + **1** = **1**

   Product: $9 \times 80 = $ **720**

Find each product mentally.

3. $5 \times 9 = $ **45**
   $5 \times 90 = $ **450**
   $5 \times 900 = $ **4,500**
   $5 \times 9,000 = $ **45,000**

4. $3 \times 6 = $ **18**
   $3 \times 60 = $ **180**
   $3 \times 600 = $ **1,800**
   $3 \times 6,000 = $ **18,000**

5. $4 \times 12 = $ **48**
   $40 \times 12 = $ **480**
   $400 \times 12 = $ **4,800**
   $4,000 \times 12 = $ **48,000**

6. $6 \times 60 = $ **360**
   $60 \times 60 = $ **3,600**
   $600 \times 60 = $ **36,000**
   $6,000 \times 60 = $ **360,000**

7. $7 \times \$3 = $ **$21**
   $70 \times \$3 = $ **$210**
   $700 \times \$3 = $ **$2,100**
   $7,000 \times \$3 = $ **$21,000**

8. $5 \times 40 = $ **200**
   $50 \times 40 = $ **2,000**
   $500 \times 40 = $ **20,000**
   $5,000 \times 40 = $ **200,000**

3–1 Skills Practice
Name _____ Date _____

Multiplication Patterns

Find each product mentally.

1. $8 \times 2 = $ **16**
   $8 \times 20 = $ **160**
   $8 \times 200 = $ **1,600**
   $8 \times 2,000 = $ **16,000**

2. $6 \times 4 = $ **24**
   $6 \times 40 = $ **240**
   $6 \times 400 = $ **2,400**
   $6 \times 4,000 = $ **24,000**

3. $4 \times 5 = $ **20**
   $4 \times 50 = $ **200**
   $4 \times 500 = $ **2,000**
   $4 \times 5,000 = $ **20,000**

4. $3 \times 80 = $ **240**
   $30 \times 80 = $ **2,400**
   $300 \times 80 = $ **24,000**
   $3,000 \times 80 = $ **240,000**

5. $5 \times 60 = $ **300**
   $50 \times 60 = $ **3,000**
   $500 \times 60 = $ **30,000**
   $5,000 \times 60 = $ **300,000**

6. $9 \times \$70 = $ **$630**
   $90 \times \$70 = $ **$6,300**
   $900 \times \$70 = $ **$63,000**
   $9,000 \times \$70 = $ **$630,000**

7. $90 \times 3 = $ **270**
8. $7 \times \$4,000 = $ **$28,000**
9. $200 \times 6 = $ **1,200**
10. $30 \times 40 = $ **1,200**
11. $600 \times 70 = $ **42,000**
12. $40 \times 800 = $ **32,000**
13. $4 \times \$1,000 = $ **$4,000**
14. $500 \times 80 = $ **40,000**
15. $70 \times 100 = $ **7,000**
16. $3 \times 30 = $ **90**
17. $5 \times 1,000 = $ **5,000**
18. $7 \times \$900 = $ **$6,300**
19. $50 \times 80 = $ **4,000**
20. $100 \times 80 = $ **8,000**
21. $50 \times 20 = $ **1,000**

Solve.

22. The 9 members of a music club in Indianapolis want to fly to New York to see several musicals. The cost of a round trip ticket is $300. How much would the airfare be altogether? **$2,700**

23. During one week, an airport shop sold 70 New York City travel guides for $9 each. How much was the total received for the guides? **$630**

Chapter Resources

3-1

Name _____ Date _____

Homework Practice

Multiplication Patterns

Find each product mentally.

1. 6 × 100 = __600__
2. 8 × 300 = __2,400__
3. 20 × 50 = __1,000__
4. 4 × 600 = __2,400__
5. 1,000 × 23 = __23,000__
6. 900 × 20 = __18,000__
7. 800 × 60 = __48,000__
8. 12 × 60 = __720__
9. 12 × 5,000 = __60,000__
10. 500 × 90 = __45,000__
11. 11 × 300 = __3,300__
12. 70 × 600 = __42,000__
13. 60 × 50 = __3,000__
14. 80 × 200 = __16,000__
15. 90 × 70 = __6,300__
16. 100 × 90 = __9,000__
17. 600 × 12 = __7,200__
18. 40 × 90 = __3,600__
19. 50 × 700 = __35,000__
20. 70 × 300 = __21,000__
21. 40 × 80 = __3,200__
22. 70 × 110 = __7,700__

Spiral Review

Add or subtract mentally. Use compensation. (Lesson 2–8)

23. 24 + 56 = __80__
24. 33 − 12 = __21__
25. 49 + 62 = __111__
26. 19 + 9 = __28__
27. 57 − 38 = __19__
28. 310 − 218 = __92__
29. 589 + 221 = __810__
30. 46 + 26 = __72__
31. 39 + 61 = __100__
32. 472 − 28 = __444__

3-1

Name _____ Date _____

Problem-Solving Practice

Multiplication Patterns

Solve.

1. There are 20 Girl Scouts. Each Girl Scout has 8 badges. How many total badges are there?

   __160 badges__

2. Lincoln Middle School ordered 60 math books. If each book costs $30, how much will the school spend?

   __$1,800__

3. Sheila is saving $8 a week for a stereo that costs $210. Will she have enough if she saves for 30 weeks?

   __Yes__

4. A music store sells 60 CDs and 40 CD players. If each CD costs $10 and each CD player costs $30, how much did the store make?

   __$1,800__

5. To find the volume of a storage chest, Dan multiplies the chest's length times its width times its height. If the chest is 20 inches wide, 20 inches high, and 40 inches long, what is the volume of the chest?

   __16,000 cubic inches__

6. Tamara is installing fence around four equal-sized square gardens. If 30 feet of fencing is needed for each garden, how many feet of fencing does Tamara need?

   __120 ft__

Answers

Answers (Lessons 3–1 and 3–2)

3–1 Enrich

Name _____ Date _____

Multiplication Patterns

Multiply the factors shown in the parentheses to complete these facts.

1. Adult great white sharks weigh about (2 × 800) **1,600** pounds and may grow to be about (4 × 5) **20** feet long.

2. The small mammal, a pygmy shrew, is only about (3 × 1) **3** inches long from head to tail.

3. The largest mammal is the blue whale. Newborn calves weigh about (20 × 300) **6,000** pounds. The heaviest adult caught weighed more than (50 × 7,000) **350,000** pounds.

4. The bat with the largest wingspan is the Bismarck flying fox. Its wingspan may be about (10 × 6) **60** inches long.

5. The largest carnivore, the polar bear, can weigh as many as (30 × 40) **1,200** pounds and have a nose-to tail length of about (5 × 20) **100** inches.

6. The fastest recorded speed of a kangaroo is (8 × 5) **40** miles per hour.

7. In the 1950s, an Arctic tern flew the longest distance ever recorded for a bird, (700 × 20) **14,000** miles.

8. In 1989, scientists recorded an elephant seal diving about (7 × 700) **4,900** feet.

9. The largest game preserve in the world is Estosha National Park in Namibia. It covers about (50 × 800) **40,000** square miles.

10. The Monterey Bay Aquarium in California has more than (600 × 600) **360,000** specimens of animals and plants.

3–2 Reteach

Name _____ Date _____

The Distributive Property

The Distributive Property combines addition and multiplication. To multiply a sum by a number, multiply each addend of the sum by the number. Then add.

Multiply 3 × 26.

Multiply and add (3 × 20) + (3 × 6).

$3 \times 26 = 3 \times (20 + 6)$
    (3 × 20)   (3 × 6)

$$3 \times 26 = 3 \times (20 + 6)$$
$$= (3 \times 20) + (3 \times 6)$$
$$= 60 + 18$$
$$= 78$$

Rewrite each expression using the Distributive Property. Then evaluate.

1. 3 × (15 + 6)
$$(3 \times 15) + (3 \times 6)$$
$$45 + 18$$
$$63$$

2. 6 × (14 + 3)
$$(6 \times 14) + (6 \times 3)$$
$$84 + 18$$
$$102$$

Find each product mentally using the Distributive Property. Show the steps that you used.

3. 2 × 48
$$2 \times (40 + 8)$$
$$(2 \times 40) + (2 \times 8)$$
$$80 + 16$$
$$96$$

4. 3 × 88
$$3 \times (80 + 8)$$
$$(3 \times 80) + (3 \times 8)$$
$$240 + 24$$
$$264$$

3–2

Name _____ Date _____

Skills Practice
The Distributive Property

Find each product mentally using the Distributive Property. Show the steps that you used.

1. 7 × 19

$7 \times (10 + 9)$

$(7 \times 10) + (7 \times 9)$

$70 + 63$

133

2. 2 × 27

$2 \times (20 + 7)$

$(2 \times 20) + (2 \times 7)$

$40 + 14$

54

3. 6 × 88

$6 \times (80 + 8)$

$(6 \times 80) + (6 \times 8)$

$480 + 48$

528

4. 9 × 98

$9 \times (90 + 8)$

$(9 \times 90) + (9 \times 8)$

$810 + 72$

882

Rewrite each expression using the Distributive Property. Then evaluate.

5. 3 × 13

$(3 \times 10) + (3 \times 3) = 39$

6. 8 × 68

$(8 \times 60) + (8 \times 8) = 544$

7. 7 × 32

$(7 \times 30) + (7 \times 2) = 224$

8. 9 × 35

$(9 \times 30) + (9 \times 5) = 315$

9. 8 × 17

$(8 \times 10) + (8 \times 7) = 136$

10. 4 × 71

$(4 \times 70) + (4 \times 1) = 284$

Solve.

11. Each of 6 hikers were allowed to bring 24 pounds of gear on a cross-country hike. How many pounds of gear was that altogether?

144 lb

12. The hikers plan to travel an average of 12 miles each day for 9 days. How many miles do they plan to travel in all?

108 mi

Grade 5   14   Chapter 3

3–2

Name _____ Date _____

Homework Practice
The Distributive Property

Rewrite each expression using the Distributive Property. Then evaluate.

1. 3 × (40 + 6)

$(3 \times 40) + (3 \times 6) = 138$

2. 6 × (60 + 5)

$(6 \times 60) + (6 \times 5) = 390$

Find each product mentally using the Distributive Property. Show the steps that you used.

3. 28 × 6

$(20 + 8) \times 6$

$(20 \times 6) + (8 \times 6)$

$120 + 48$

168

4. 6 × 34

$6 \times (30 + 4)$

$(6 \times 30) + (6 + 4)$

$180 + 24$

204

5. 35 × 7

$(30 + 5) \times 7$

$(30 \times 7) + (5 \times 7)$

$210 + 35$

245

6. 3 × 72

$3 \times (70 + 2)$

$(3 \times 70) + (3 \times 2)$

$210 + 6$

216

7. Mrs. Robertson bought 7 tickets for the school play on Monday and 5 tickets on Tuesday. Each ticket was $6. How much did she spend on the tickets? Show how you can use the Distributive Property.

$\$6 \times (7 + 5) = (\$6 \times 7) +$
$(\$6 \times 5) = \$42 + \$30 = \$72$

8. In each package of school supplies there are 3 notebooks and 2 pencils. If you have 42 packages, how many notebooks and pencils do you have altogether? Use the Distributive Property and show your steps.

$5 \times 42; (5 \times 40) + (5 \times 2);$
$200 + 10 = 210; 210$ **notebooks and pencils**

Spiral Review
Find each product mentally. (Lesson 3–1)

9. 10 × 18

180

10. 24 × 60

1,440

11. 300 × 9

2,700

12. 50 × 15

750

Grade 5   15   Chapter 3

Answers (Lesson 3–2)

Problem-Solving Practice (3–2)

Name _____ Date _____

The Distributive Property

Solve.

1. Ray needs to multiply 5 × 26 to find the area of a rectangle. To use the distributive property, how would you fill in the blanks?

$5 \times 26 = 5 \times (\underline{20} + 6)$
$= (5 \times \underline{20}) + (5 \times 6)$
$= \underline{100} + 30$
$= \underline{130}$

2. To multiply 8 × 14, Jana used the distributive property. Fill in the blanks to show what she did:

$8 \times 14 = 8 \times (10 + \underline{4})$
$= (8 \times \underline{10}) + (8 \times 4)$
$= \underline{80} + 32$
$= \underline{112}$

3. Four friends went out to dinner. To cover dinner, tax, and tip, each person paid $18. How much did they pay altogether?

$72

4. The fifth-grade classes at Wilcox Elementary School are reading books during the summer. There are 76 students, and each is supposed to read 4 books. How many books will the students read in all?

304 books

5. The four Boy Scout troops in Carver City sold 1,238 buckets of popcorn to raise money. If each bucket costs $4, how much money did the troops raise?

$4,952

6. James builds and sells furniture. Last month he sold 9 bookcases and 6 coffee tables. If each bookcase costs $310, and each coffee table costs $275, how much did James make?

$4,440

Enrich (3–2)

Name _____ Date _____

The Distributive Property and Subtraction

The Distributive Property can also be used to combine subtraction and multiplication. To multiply the difference of two numbers by a number, multiply each term in the parentheses by the number. Then subtract.

$3 \times (5 - 2) = (3 \times 5) - (3 \times 2)$ Use the Distributive Property to rewrite the expression.
$= 15 - 6$ Multiply the numbers in parentheses.
$= 9$ Subtract.

You can use the Distributive Property and subtraction to find a product like 2 × 79 mentally.

$2 \times 79 = 2 \times (80 - 1)$ Write 79 as 80 − 1.
$= (2 \times 80) - (2 \times 1)$ Distributive Property
$= 160 - 2$ Find 2 × 80 and 2 × 1 mentally.
$= 158$ Find 160 − 2 mentally.

Rewrite each expression using the Distributive Property. Then evaluate.

1. 3 × (20 − 1)   **$(3 \times 20) - (3 \times 1)$; 57**

2. 2 × (10 − 1)   **$(2 \times 10) - (2 \times 1)$; 18**

3. 5 × (30 − 2)   **$(5 \times 30) - (5 \times 2)$; 140**

Find each product mentally using the Distributive Property and subtraction. Show the steps that you used.

4. 2 × 29

$2 \times 29 = 2 \times (30 - 1)$
$= (2 \times 30) - (2 \times 1)$
$= 60 - 2$
$= 58$

5. 3 × 48

$3 \times 48 = 3 \times (50 - 2)$
$= (3 \times 50) - (3 \times 2)$
$= 150 - 6$
$= 144$

Reteach 3-3

Name _____ Date _____

Reteach
Estimate Products

To estimate a product, round each number. Then use a basic fact and a multiplication pattern to multiply mentally.

Estimate 27 × 643.   Estimate 54 × 761

Round each number to its greatest place.

27 × 643 $\rightarrow$
$\rightarrow$ 700 × 40 = 28,000

54 × 761

Write the basic fact. Then, write the same number of zeros in the product as are in both factors.

30 × 600 = 18,000   50 × 800 = 40,000
1 zero + 2 zeros = 3 zeros   1 zero + 2 zeros = 3 zeros

Estimate by rounding. Show your work.

1. 54 × 68   50 × 70 = 3,500
2. 61 × 239   60 × 200 = 12,000
3. 697 × 43   700 × 40 = 28,000
4. 364 × 28   400 × 30 = 12,000
5. 8 × 674   8 × 700 = 5,600
6. 9 × 458   9 × 500 = 4,500
7. 43 × 104   40 × 100 = 4,000
8. 19 × 74   20 × 70 = 1,400
9. 84 × 13   80 × 10 = 800
10. 21 × 663   20 × 700 = 14,000
11. 38 × 573   40 × 600 = 24,000
12. 18 × 264   20 × 300 = 6,000
13. 184 × 48   200 × 50 = 10,000
14. 26 × 904   30 × 900 = 27,000

Grade 5   18   Chapter 3

Skills Practice 3-3

Name _____ Date _____

Skills Practice
Estimate Products

Estimate by rounding. Show your work.

1. 34 × 10   30 × 10 = 300
2. 59 × 32   60 × 30 = 1,800
3. 446 × 682   400 × 700 = 280,000
4. 21 × 663   20 × 700 = 14,000
5. 98 × 32   100 × 30 = 3,000
6. 91 × 32   100 × 30 = 3,000
7. 334 × 847   300 × 800 = 240,000
8. 929 × 8   900 × 10 = 9,000
9. 43 × 58   40 × 60 = 2,400
10. 186 × 92   200 × 90 = 18,000
11. 342 × 86   300 × 90 = 27,000
12. 396 × 23   400 × 20 = 8,000

13. 8,547
    × 836   9,000 × 800 = 7,200,000
14. 603
    × 29   600 × 30 = 18,000
15. 408
    × 46   400 × 50 = 20,000
16. 3,045
    × 38   3,000 × 40 = 120,000

Estimate by using compatible numbers. Show your work.

17. 6 × 24   6 × 25 = 150
18. 8 × 48   8 × 50 = 400
19. 12 × 26   12 × 25 = 300
20. 12 × 52   12 × 50 = 600
21. 110 × 97   100 × 100 = 10,000
22. 120 × 11   120 × 10 = 1,200

Solve.

23. Tickets to a basketball game cost $22 each. Mr. Reynolds bought 17 tickets to give away as prizes at an assembly. About how much did the tickets cost altogether?

about $400

24. There are 514 students at Scioto Elementary. Each of the students donated 7 food items for a charity food drive. About how many items were collected altogether?

about 5,000 items

Grade 5   19   Chapter 3

Name _____ Date _____

3-3

Problem-Solving Practice

Estimate Products

Solve.

1. Val bought 12 DVDs at $18 each. Estimate the total cost of the DVDs.

   about $200

2. Eric's dog weighs 27 pounds, Tina's dog weighs 33 pounds, and Emir's dog weighs 29 pounds. Estimate the total weight of all three dogs.

   about 90 lb

3. On a cross-country vacation, Maria filled her 14-gallon gas tank 11 times. About how many gallons of gas did she put in the tank altogether?

   about 100 gal

4. Sven went on an 8 day vacation to Hong Kong. He took enough money with him so that he could spend $73 per day. About how much money did he take on vacation?

   about $700

5. Sherry has a jogging route through her neighborhood. She ran this route for 22 days in April, 20 days in May, and 19 days in June. Estimate the total number of days she ran.

   about 60 days

6. Klara is visiting relatives in Norway and then Sweden. First, she exchanged $184 U.S dollars for Norwegian kroner. Then she exchanged $192 for Swedish krona. Finally, she exchanged another $212 for Swedish krona. About how much did she exchange altogether?

   about $600

Name _____ Date _____

3-3

Homework Practice

Estimate Products

Estimate by rounding. Show your work.

1. 542
   × 38

   $500 \times 40 =$ **20,000**

2. 821
   × 14

   $800 \times 10 =$ **8,000**

3. 726
   × 38

   $700 \times 40 =$ **28,000**

4. 174
   × 73

   $200 \times 70 =$ **14,000**

5. 2,862
   × 143

   $3,000 \times 100 =$ **300,000**

6. 12,649
   × 382

   $13,000 \times 400 =$ **5,200,000**

7. 69,238
   × 54

   $70,000 \times 50 = 3,500,000$

8. 10,405
   × 632

   $10,000 \times 600 = 6,000,000$

9. 14×77 $10 \times 80 =$ **800**

10. 34×873 $30 \times 900 =$ **27,000**

11. 469×18 $500 \times 20 =$ **10,000**

12. 89×806 $90 \times 800 =$ **72,000**

13. 47×962 $50 \times 1,000 =$ **50,000**

14. $3,721 \times 499$ $4,000 \times 500 =$ **2,000,000**

15. $198 \times 2,203$ $200 \times 2,000 =$ **400,000**

16. $3,926 \times 198$ $4,000 \times 200 =$ **800,000**

Spiral Review

Rewrite each expression using the Distributive Property. Then evaluate. (Lesson 3-2)

17. $6 \times (10 + 5)$
    $(6 \times 10) + (6 \times 5) =$ **90**

18. $4 \times (30 + 6)$
    $(4 \times 30) + (4 \times 6) =$ **144**

19. $3 \times (30 + 8)$
    $(3 \times 30) + (3 \times 8) =$ **114**

20. $7 \times (40 + 6)$
    $(7 \times 40) + (7 \times 6) =$ **322**

21. $2 \times (10 + 7)$
    $(2 \times 10) + (2 \times 7) =$ **34**

22. $6 \times (40 + 8)$
    $(6 \times 40) + (6 \times 8) =$ **288**

3-3

Name _____ Date _____

Enrich

Estimate Products

Choose a factor from the box to give each estimated product. You can use a number more than once.

224	789	17	322
72	9	495	914

1. 483 × **322**
   About 150,000

2. 68 × **72**
   About 4,900

3. 196 × **789**
   About 160,000

4. 213 × **495**
   About 100,000

5. 14 × **9**
   About 100

6. 287 × **224**
   About 60,000

7. 12 × **17**
   About 200

8. 28 × **495**
   About 15,000

9. 23 × **914**
   About 18,000

10. 96 × **17**
   About 2,000

11. 2 × 24 × **914**
   About 45,000

12. 28 × **789** × 8
   About 240,000

Look at the numbers in the box.

13. Which two factors would give the least product?   **9 and 17**

14. Which three factors would give the greatest product?
   914, 789, and 495

3-4

Name _____ Date _____

Reteach

Multiply by One-Digit Numbers

Find 32 × 6.
Estimate: 32 × 6 = 180

Step 1	Step 2

Multiply the ones.

$$\begin{array}{r} \overset{1}{3}2 \\ \times\ 6 \\ \hline 2 \end{array}$$

6 × 2 = 12 ones

Multiply the tens.

$$\begin{array}{r} \overset{1}{3}2 \\ \times\ 6 \\ \hline 192 \end{array}$$

6 × 3 = 18 tens
18 + 1 = 19 tens

The product is 192. This is close to the estimate of 180, so the answer is reasonable.

Multiply.

1. $\begin{array}{r} 53 \\ \times\ 4 \\ \hline 212 \end{array}$

2. $\begin{array}{r} 26 \\ \times\ 3 \\ \hline 78 \end{array}$

3. $\begin{array}{r} 38 \\ \times\ 5 \\ \hline 190 \end{array}$

4. $\begin{array}{r} 47 \\ \times\ 4 \\ \hline 188 \end{array}$

5. $\begin{array}{r} 12 \\ \times\ 3 \\ \hline 36 \end{array}$

6. $\begin{array}{r} 28 \\ \times\ 6 \\ \hline 168 \end{array}$

7. $\begin{array}{r} 144 \\ \times\ 3 \\ \hline 432 \end{array}$

8. $\begin{array}{r} 615 \\ \times\ 4 \\ \hline 2,460 \end{array}$

9. $\begin{array}{r} 262 \\ \times\ 5 \\ \hline 1,310 \end{array}$

10. $\begin{array}{r} 811 \\ \times\ 2 \\ \hline 1,622 \end{array}$

11. $\begin{array}{r} 501 \\ \times\ 6 \\ \hline 3,006 \end{array}$

12. $\begin{array}{r} 149 \\ \times\ 7 \\ \hline 1,043 \end{array}$

13. 5 × 78

$$\begin{array}{r} 390 \end{array}$$

14. 24 × 6

$$\begin{array}{r} 144 \end{array}$$

15. 704 × 3

$$\begin{array}{r} 2,112 \end{array}$$

16. 8 × 92

$$\begin{array}{r} 736 \end{array}$$

Answers

3–4 Homework Practice
Multiply by One-Digit Numbers

Name _____ Date _____

Multiply.

1. $47 \times 3 = 141$
2. $28 \times 2 = 56$
3. $65 \times 5 = 325$
4. $41 \times 4 = 164$
5. $6 \times 37 = 222$
6. $25 \times 8 = 200$
7. $94 \times 7 = 658$
8. $4 \times 38 = 152$
9. $249 \times 6 = 1{,}494$
10. $326 \times 2 = 652$
11. $3 \times 547 = 1{,}641$
12. $683 \times 3 = 2{,}049$
13. $552 \times 3 = 1{,}656$
14. $243 \times 4 = 972$
15. $671 \times 7 = 4{,}697$
16. $342 \times 2 = 684$
17. $128 \times 6 = 768$
18. $444 \times 5 = 2{,}220$
19. $831 \times 7 = 5{,}817$
20. $756 \times 2 = 1{,}512$

Spiral Review
Estimate by rounding. Show your work. (Lesson 3–3)

21. 107×54; $100 \times 50 = 5{,}000$
22. 38×7; $40 \times 10 = 400$
23. 602×14; $600 \times 10 = 6{,}000$
24. 68×69; $70 \times 70 = 4{,}900$
25. 42×51; $40 \times 50 = 2{,}000$
26. 216×7; $200 \times 10 = 2{,}000$
27. 19×19; $20 \times 20 = 400$
28. 401×33; $400 \times 30 = 12{,}000$

3–4 Skills Practice
Multiply by One-Digit Numbers

Name _____ Date _____

Multiply.

1. $83 \times 5 = 415$
2. $66 \times 6 = 396$
3. $32 \times 4 = 128$
4. $44 \times 3 = 132$
5. $56 \times 5 = 280$
6. $14 \times 7 = 98$
7. $28 \times 4 = 112$
8. $89 \times 2 = 178$
9. $557 \times 9 = 5{,}013$
10. $732 \times 6 = 4{,}392$
11. $645 \times 3 = 1{,}935$
12. $312 \times 2 = 624$
13. $564 \times 4 = 2{,}256$
14. $623 \times 7 = 4{,}361$
15. $769 \times 3 = 2{,}307$
16. $293 \times 6 = 1{,}758$
17. $4 \times 39 = 156$
18. $19 \times 8 = 152$
19. $344 \times 7 = 2{,}408$
20. $3 \times 51 = 153$
21. $2 \times 99 = 198$
22. $63 \times 3 = 189$
23. $519 \times 4 = 2{,}076$
24. $4 \times 89 = 356$
25. $2 \times 67 = 134$
26. $42 \times 5 = 210$
27. $716 \times 8 = 5{,}728$
28. $6 \times 191 = 1{,}146$

29. The math club at Southview Elementary School sold 443 rolls of wrapping paper during the holiday fundraiser. If the price of each roll was $4, how much money did they earn? **$1,772**

30. Andrea made 28 flowerpots to sell at the craft fair. Jenna made twice as many flowerpots. How many flower pots does Jenna have? **56 flowerpots**

Answers (Lesson 3–4)

Name _____ Date _____

3-4 Enrich

The Greatest Product Game

The goal of this game is to make up the greatest product.

Get Ready!

Players: 2 to 4
You Will Need: 10 index cards

Get Set!

- Write a different digit from 0 to 9 on each card.
- Mix up the cards. Then place the cards in a pile facedown.
- Each player should draw four boxes on a piece of paper as shown.

Go!

- Each player takes a turn choosing a card.
- The player writes the digit on the card in one of the boxes on his or her paper. Players may not move digits after they have placed them in a box.
- When all the boxes are full, players should find their products.
- The player with the greatest product is the winner.

Name _____ Date _____

3-4 Problem-Solving Practice

Multiply by One-Digit Numbers

1. Karen and Anthony are setting up rows for the piano recital. They set up 22 rows with 6 chairs in each row. How many total people will the rows seat?

132 people

2. Each student in Mrs. Henderson's science class brought in 3 books for the book donation. If there are 25 students in the class, how many total books did they collect?

75 books

3. There are 36 teams in the baseball league. Each team has 9 players on its roster. How many total players are there?

324 players

4. Alex, Brianna, and Jonathan each have $29 to spend on a birthday gift for their mother. How much money do they have in all?

$87

5. The Community Center purchased 7 new exercise machines for the gym. Each machine cost $269. What was the total cost?

$1,883

6. One city bus can carry 72 passengers. Will three city buses be able to carry 250 passengers? Explain.

No. Three buses will hold 216 passengers.

Name _____ Date _____

3–5 Reteach

Problem-Solving Strategy

Draw a picture.

Step 3 Solve	Draw four small squares so that they form one large square.
	Draw one circle at each exposed edge of each small square.
	How many people can sit at four tables pushed together in a square? **8 people**
Step 4 Check	**Is the solution reasonable?** Reread the problem.
	Have you answered the question? **yes**
	How can you decide if your results are reasonable?
	Possible answer: The number of seats is greater than the number of seats at one small table. But it is less than the number of seats at tables that are not pushed together. So, the results are reasonable.

Solve.

1. A restaurant has some circular tables and three large square tables. Two people can sit on each side of a large square table. If the three large square tables are pushed together to form a rectangle, how many people can sit at the rectangle?

   16 people

2. A house has a rectangular porch that is 15 feet by 20 feet. One of the long sides of the porch is connected to the house. The other sides of the porch have a 2-foot high railing. What is the total length of the railing?

   50 ft

Grade 5   29   Chapter 3

Name _____ Date _____

3–5 Reteach

Problem-Solving Strategy: Draw a picture

You are making a seating chart for a math center. If one person can sit on each side of a square table, how many people can sit at four tables pushed together in a square?

Step 1 Understand	**Be sure you understand the problem.** Read carefully.
	What do you know?
	• There are **four** square tables.
	• **One person** can sit on each side of a square table.
	What do you need to find?
	• You need to find the number of people **who can sit at four tables pushed together in a square.**
Step 2 Plan	**Make a plan.** Choose a strategy.
• Draw a Picture	You can draw a picture to solve the problem.
• Guess and Check	You can use four small squares to represent the tables. You
• Work Backward	can use a circle to represent each chair.

Grade 5   28   Chapter 3

3-5

Name _____ Date _____

Skills Practice

Problem-Solving Strategy: Draw a picture

Solve. Use the draw a picture strategy.

1. Maria wants to tack three rectangular pictures in a row on the bulletin board. The edges of the pictures can overlap. Maria wants to put a tack in each corner of each picture. How many tacks does she need?

   8 tacks

2. Jack builds a patio from square tiles that are 2 feet on each side. The patio is 10 feet by 16 feet. How many tiles does Jack need in order to build the patio?

   40 tiles

3. Howard leaves the dock and sails 2.5 miles west. He turns south and sails 3.5 miles. Then he turns east and sails 2.5 miles. In what direction should Howard turn if he wants to use the most direct route to return to the dock? If Howard uses this route, how many miles will he have sailed in all?

   north; 12 miles

4. The main lawn of a college is a rectangle with one building on each side. There is a path from each building to each of the other buildings. How many paths are there?

   6

5. Akira cut triangles of the same size out of different colors of cloth. She is going to use the pieces to make a quilt. She places the triangles together around one point until they form a hexagon. How many of the triangles did she have to use?

   6 triangles

6. For every two steps her dad takes, Heidi takes 4 steps. How many steps will she takes if her dad takes 30 steps?

   60 steps

Grade 5   30   Chapter 3

3-5

Name _____ Date _____

Homework Practice

Problem-Solving Strategy: Draw a picture

Solve. Use the draw a picture strategy.

1. Gregory arranges eight identical cubes into one large cube on a table. How many sides of the small cubes can he see?

   20 sides

2. Al walks 3 blocks north, 2 blocks east, 3 blocks north, and 3 blocks east to get to the theater. Will the path home be any shorter if he walks south to his street, then west to his house? Why?

   No; The walk will be 11 blocks either way.

3. Sandy's classroom has tables that are shaped like rectangles. Three of the tables are placed together in a U-shape. One student can sit at the short side of each rectangle or at the end of a table. Two students can sit at the long side of each rectangle. No students sit along the "inside" of the U-shape. How many students can sit at the tables the way they are arranged?

   10 students

4. Valerie is making coasters for her mother's craft booth. For each coaster, she uses a square of cork and four pieces of wood to glue along the edges. If she has 25 pieces of cork and 92 pieces of wood, how many coasters can she make?

   23 coasters

   Will she run out of the cork first or the wood?

   wood

Spiral Review

Estimate. Then Multiply. (Lesson 3–4)

5. 68
   × 4
   272

6. 59
   × 6
   354

7. 519
   × 3
   1,557

8. 874
   × 2
   1,748

9. 338
   × 5
   1,690

10. 902
   × 3
   2,706

Grade 5   31   Chapter 3

Answers

3–6 Reteach

Name _____ Date _____

Multiply by Two-Digit Numbers

Find 265 × 21.
Estimate: 300 × 20 = 6,000

Step 1 Multiply the ones.	Step 2 Multiply the tens.	Step 3 Add.
265	265	265
× 21	× 21	× 21
————	————	————
265 265 × 1 = 265	265	265
	5300 265 × 20 = 5,300	5300
		5,565 265 + 5,300 = 5,565

So, 265 × 21 = 5,565.

Multiply.

1. $\begin{array}{r} 45 \\ \times\ 12 \\ \hline 540 \end{array}$
2. $\begin{array}{r} 68 \\ \times\ 33 \\ \hline 2{,}244 \end{array}$
3. $\begin{array}{r} 57 \\ \times\ 19 \\ \hline 1{,}083 \end{array}$
4. $\begin{array}{r} 24 \\ \times\ 39 \\ \hline 936 \end{array}$
5. $\begin{array}{r} 72 \\ \times\ 46 \\ \hline 3{,}312 \end{array}$

6. $\begin{array}{r} 68 \\ \times\ 34 \\ \hline 2{,}312 \end{array}$
7. $\begin{array}{r} 25 \\ \times\ 25 \\ \hline 625 \end{array}$
8. $\begin{array}{r} 82 \\ \times\ 58 \\ \hline 4{,}756 \end{array}$
9. $\begin{array}{r} 93 \\ \times\ 37 \\ \hline 3{,}441 \end{array}$
10. $\begin{array}{r} 81 \\ \times\ 93 \\ \hline 7{,}533 \end{array}$

11. $\begin{array}{r} 364 \\ \times\ 87 \\ \hline 31{,}668 \end{array}$
12. $\begin{array}{r} 617 \\ \times\ 62 \\ \hline 38{,}254 \end{array}$
13. $\begin{array}{r} 703 \\ \times\ 29 \\ \hline 20{,}387 \end{array}$
14. $\begin{array}{r} 548 \\ \times\ 95 \\ \hline 52{,}060 \end{array}$
15. $\begin{array}{r} 277 \\ \times\ 38 \\ \hline 10{,}526 \end{array}$

16. $\begin{array}{r} 229 \\ \times\ 43 \\ \hline 9{,}847 \end{array}$
17. $\begin{array}{r} 326 \\ \times\ 55 \\ \hline 17{,}930 \end{array}$
18. $\begin{array}{r} 449 \\ \times\ 39 \\ \hline 17{,}511 \end{array}$
19. $\begin{array}{r} 622 \\ \times\ 12 \\ \hline 7{,}464 \end{array}$
20. $\begin{array}{r} 882 \\ \times\ 59 \\ \hline 52{,}038 \end{array}$

3–5 Enrich

Name _____ Date _____

Exponents

While working on a family tree project to trace his family's roots, Tim wanted to know how many great-great-grandparents he has.

Family Members	Parents	Grandparents	Great-grandparents	Great-great-grandparents
Number	2	2 × 2 = 4	2 × 2 × 2 = 8	2 × 2 × 2 × 2 = 16

So, Tim has 2 × 2 × 2 × 2 or 16 great-great-grandparents.

When a product like 2 × 2 × 2 × 2 has identical factors, you can use an exponent to write the product. An **exponent** describes how many times a number is used as a factor.

2 factors
$2 \times 2 = 2^2$ Exponent is 2.

3 factors
$2 \times 2 \times 2 = 2^3$ Exponent is 3.

4 factors
$2 \times 2 \times 2 \times 2 = 2^4$ Exponent is 4.

Rewrite each product using an exponent. Then evaluate.

1. $3 \times 3 \times 3 \times 3$ 3^4; 81
2. $5 \times 5 \times 5$ 5^3; 125
3. $4 \times 4 \times 4 \times 4 \times 4$ 4^5; 1,024
4. $2 \times 2 \times 2 \times 2 \times 2 \times 2 \times 2$ 2^7; 128

Rewrite each as a multiplication expression. Then evaluate.

5. 9^2 9×9; 81
6. 6^5 $6 \times 6 \times 6 \times 6 \times 6$; 7,776
7. 10^3 $10 \times 10 \times 10$; 1,000
8. 3^6 $3 \times 3 \times 3 \times 3 \times 3 \times 3$; 729

ALGEBRA Find each missing number.

9. $7^{\square} = 49$ 2
10. $\square^2 = 64$ 8
11. $\square^5 = 32$ 2
12. $5^{\square} = 625$ 4
13. $\square^1 = 15$ 15
14. $12^{\square} = 1{,}728$ 3

Answers (Lesson 3–6)

3-6 Skills Practice

Name _____ Date _____

Multiply by Two-Digit Numbers

Multiply.

1. 32 × 517 = **16,544**
2. 466 × 21 = **9,786**
3. 83 × 13 = **1,079**
4. 43 × 65 = **2,795**
5. 458 × 26 = **11,908**
6. 329 × 72 = **23,688**
7. 601 × 24 = **14,424**
8. 728 × 68 = **49,504**
9. 188 × 46 = **8,648**
10. 250 × 27 = **6,750**
11. 45 × 371 = **16,695**
12. 70 × 686 = **48,020**

13. 67 × 211 = **14,137**
14. 30 × 456 = **13,680**
15. 170 × 55 = **9,350**
16. 824 × 19 = **15,656**
17. 345 × 42 = **14,490**

18. $740 × 16 = **$11,840**
19. 92 × 301 = **27,692**
20. 262 × 39 = **10,218**
21. 114 × 48 = **5,472**
22. 653 × 20 = **13,060**

23. 49 × 700 = **34,300**
24. 318 × 52 = **16,536**
25. 202 × 96 = **19,392**
26. 79 × 349 = **27,571**
27. 26 × 781 = **20,306**

28. 176 × 45 = **7,920**
29. 500 × 19 = **9,500**
30. 241 × 67 = **16,147**
31. 82 × 820 = **67,240**
32. 199 × 36 = **7,164**

Solve.

33. A basketball player scored an average of 23 points per game. He played 82 games during the season. How many points did he score that season? **1,886 points**

34. A basketball arena has 36 sections of seats. Each section contains 784 seats. How many people can the arena seat? **28,224 people**

3-6 Homework Practice

Name _____ Date _____

Multiply by Two-Digit Numbers

Multiply.

1. 142 × 65 = **9,230**
2. 407 × 73 = **29,711**
3. $396 × 84 = **$33,264**
4. 862 × 29 = **24,998**
5. 64 × 981 = **62,784**
6. 69 × 46 = **3,174**
7. 57 × $37 = **$2,109**
8. 656 × 23 = **15,088**
9. 390 × 48 = **18,720**
10. 357 × 54 = **19,278**
11. 378 × 76 = **28,728**
12. 476 × 93 = **44,268**
13. 73 × $547 = **$39,931**
14. 326 × 57 = **18,582**
15. 318 × 21 = **6,678**
16. 215 × 58 = **12,470**
17. 19 × $739 = **$14,041**
18. 862 × 12 = **10,344**
19. 84 × 119 = **9,996**
20. 37 × 208 = **7,696**
21. 239 × 17 = **4,063**
22. 926 × 60 = **55,560**
23. 85 × 63 = **5,355**
24. 209 × 75 = **15,675**
25. 45 × 306 = **13,770**
26. 443 × 19 = **8,417**

Spiral Review

Solve. Use the *draw a picture strategy*. (Lesson 3–5)

27. Tulips are planted every 4 feet around the outside edge of a rectangular garden. If the sides of the garden measure 16 feet and 12 feet, how many total tulips are there? **14 tulips**

28. Jill has 5 pictures to hang on her wall. She wants to hang one picture in the center and the other 4 at the corners of the center picture. If the picture in the center remains the same, how many different ways can she hang the other pictures? **24 ways**

Answers

Answers (Lesson 3–6)

Problem-Solving Practice 3-6

Name _____ Date _____

3-6

Problem-Solving Practice
Multiply by Two-Digit Numbers

Solve.

1. Gary and Cedric are taking a 14-day road trip. They plan to drive 130 miles each day. How many miles would this be?

1,820 miles

2. This summer, Jane worked for 10 weeks at her mother's book store. She earned $150 per week. How much did Jane earn?

$1,500

3. The owners of Pizza Palace, a new restaurant, need to order furniture for their dining room. They need 26 tables and 120 chairs. How much will the tables and chairs cost if each table costs $43 and each chair costs $22?

$3,758

4. For his job, Robert flies from Dallas, Texas, to Austin, Texas 25 times a year. If the round-trip flight between the two cities is 362 miles, how many total miles does Robert fly in a year?

9,050 miles

5. Emily has a compact car that gets 38 miles per gallon of gas. Marcello's station wagon gets 29 miles per gallon. Emily's car holds 12 gallons of gas and Marcello's holds 15 gallons. Who can travel farther on a full tank of gas?

Emily's car will go 21 miles farther

6. Theresa commutes to work 16 days each month. She travels 56 miles round trip. Carl commutes to work 20 days each month; he also travels 56 miles round trip. Theresa works 12 months of the year, and Carl works 11 months. Who travels more in one year?

Carl travels 1,568 miles farther each year

Grade 5   36   Chapter 3

Enrich 3-6

Name _____ Date _____

3-6

Enrich
Multiply by Two-Digit Numbers

Play a multiplication game with a partner.

How to Play

- Choose a number from one of the circles and from one of the squares. Use the numbers to write a number sentence to fit each description below. Then find the product of the numbers.
- Work quickly. Your partner will record the time you used to finish the exercise.
- Switch roles. The player who uses less time wins the game.

(83)   [532]

1. the least product

$$6 \times 357 = 2{,}142$$

[2,178]   (57)

2. the greatest product

$$83 \times 42{,}133 = 3{,}497{,}039$$

(9)   [357]

3. two different products with a zero in the ones place

$$45 \times 532 = 23{,}940; \ 45 \times 2{,}178 = 98{,}010$$

[921]

4. the greatest product with an 8 in the ones place

$$28 \times 26{,}401 = 739{,}228$$

(6)   (28)

5. the least product with a 9 in the ones place

$$9 \times 921 = 8{,}289$$

6. the product with a 3 as the first and last digit

$$9 \times 357 = 3{,}213$$

(72)   [7,059]

7. two different products between 30,000 and 40,000

$$57 \times 532 = 30{,}324; \ 72 \times 532 = 38{,}304$$

[42,133]   (45)

8. the product closest to 60,000

$$28 \times 2{,}178 = 60{,}984$$

[26,041]

9. the product closest to 300,000

$$45 \times 7{,}059 = 317{,}655$$

Your time: _____

Your partner's time: _____

Grade 5   37   Chapter 3

Reteach 3–7
Multiplication Properties

Name _____ Date _____

You can use these multiplication properties to find products mentally.

Commutative Property	Associative Property	Identity Property
The order of the factors does not change the product.	The way the factors are grouped does not change the product.	The product of any number and 1 is that number.
$25 \times 4 = 4 \times 25$ $100 = 100$	$(9 \times 4) \times 5 = 9 \times (4 \times 5)$ $36 \times 5 = 9 \times 20$ $180 = 180$	$87 \times 1 = 87$ $1 \times 6.5 = 6.5$

Identify the multiplication property used to rewrite each problem.

1. $(3 \times 5) \times 2 = 3 \times (5 \times 2)$
   Associative Property

2. $6 \times 2 \times 18 = 6 \times 18 \times 2$
   Commutative Property

3. $13 \times 24 \times 9 = 9 \times 24 \times 13$
   Commutative Property

4. $(15 \times 6) \times 3 = 15 \times (6 \times 3)$
   Associative Property

Use properties of multiplication to find each product mentally. Show your steps and identify the properties that you used.

5. $25 \times 9 \times 4$
   $25 \times 4 \times 9$ Commutative
   $(25 \times 4) \times 9$ Associative
   100×9 Find 25×4 mentally.
   900 Find 100×9 mentally.

6. $(19 \times 5) \times 2$
   $19 \times (5 \times 2)$ Associative
   19×10 Find 5×2 mentally.
   190 Find 19×10 mentally.

7. $9 \times 29 \times 0$
   $9 \times (29 \times 0)$ Associative
   9×0 Find 29×0 mentally.
   0 Find 9×0 mentally.

8. $(4 \times 15) \times 2$
   $4 \times (15 \times 2)$ Associative
   4×30 Find 15×2 mentally.
   120 Find 4×30 mentally.

Skills Practice 3–7
Multiplication Properties

Name _____ Date _____

Identify the multiplication property used to rewrite each problem.

1. $(185 \times 6) \times \underline{\quad} = 185 \times (6 \times 2)$
   Associative Property

2. $9 \times (60 + 7) = (\underline{\quad} \times 60) + (9 \times 7)$
   Distributive Property

3. $124 \times \underline{\quad} = 14 \times 124$
   Commutative Property

4. $3.41 \times \underline{\quad} = 3.41$
   Identity Property

Use properties of multiplication to find each product mentally. Show your steps and identify the properties that you used.

5. $5 \times 24 \times 2$
   $5 \times 2 \times 24$ Commutative
   $(5 \times 2) \times 24$ Associative
   10×24 Find 5×2 mentally.
   240 Find 10×24 mentally.

6. $200 \times (4 \times 7)$
   $(200 \times 4) \times 7$ Associative
   800×7 Find 200×4 mentally.
   $5,600$ Find 800×7 mentally.

7. $483 \times 10 \times 1$
   $(483 \times 10) \times 1$ Associative
   $4,830 \times 1$ Find 483×10 mentally.
   $4,830$ Identity

8. $5 \times 3 \times 20$
   $5 \times 20 \times 3$ Commutative
   $(5 \times 20) \times 3$ Associative
   100×3 Find 5×20 mentally.
   300 Find 100×3 mentally.

Answers

Answers (Lesson 3–7)

3-7 Problem-Solving Practice
Multiplication Properties

Solve.

1. Eva needs to multiply 1 × 245. Give the product and name the property she would use.

   245; Identity Property

2. Jose needs to multiply three numbers: (6 × 14) × 2. Give the product and name the property he would use.

   168; Associative Property

Find the number that makes the sentence true.

3. Alicia uses the Commutative Property to find n.

   15 × 4 = n × 15

   4

4. Peter uses the Associative Property to find n.

   (35 × 2) × 8 = 35 × (n × 8)

   n = 2

Solve.

5. During the summer, Henry read two books. The first book had 148 pages. The second book had twice as many pages. Henry's older brother read only one book, but it had twice as many pages as Henry's second book. Did Henry's brother read more or less than Henry?

   More

6. The population of Delaware in the year 2000 was 783,600. The state has three counties: Kent, New Castle, and Sussex. Kent County has 126,697 people and New Castle has 500,265. Is the total population of Kent and New Castle counties more than four times the population of Sussex County?

   Yes

Grade 5   41   Chapter 3

3-7 Homework Practice
Multiplication Properties

Identify the multiplication property used to rewrite each problem.

1. (81 × 4) × 5 = 81 × (4 × 5)

   Associative Property

2. (28 × 7) × 16 = 28 × (7 × 16)

   Associative Property

3. 15 × 8 = 8 × 15

   Commutative Property

4. 72 × 1 = 72

   Identity Property

Use properties of multiplication to find each product mentally. Show your steps and identify the properties that you used.

5. 76 × 25 × 4

   76 × (25 × 4) **Associative**

   76 × 100   **Find 25 × 4 mentally.**

   7,600   **Find 76 × 100 mentally.**

6. 5 × 60 × 20

   5 × 20 × 60 **Commutative**

   (5 × 20) × 60 **Associative**

   100 × 60   **Find 5 × 20 mentally.**

   6,000   **Find 100 × 60 mentally.**

7. 40 × 0 × 17

   (42 × 0) × 17 **Associative**

   0 × 17   **Find 42 × 0 mentally.**

   0   **Find 0 × 17 mentally.**

8. 2 × 4 × 12

   2 × (4 × 12) **Associative**

   2 × 48   **Find 4 × 12 mentally.**

   96   **Find 2 × 48 mentally.**

Spiral Review

Multiply. (Lesson 3–6)

9. 560 × 24 = **13,440**

10. 68 × 17 = **1,156**

11. 341 × 25 = **8,525**

12. 18 × 49 = **882**

13. 836 × 32 = **26,752**

14. 95 × 73 = **6,935**

15. 188 × 58 = **10,904**

16. 712 × 65 = **46,280**

Grade 5   40   Chapter 3

3–8 Reteach

Name _____ Date _____

Extending Multiplication

Margaret would like to buy 4 notebooks that cost $3.08 a piece. The total cost will be 4 × $3.08. You can estimate the total cost using rounding.

4 × $3.08

4 × $3 — Round $3.08 to $3 because $3.08 is closer to $3 than $4.

4 × $3 = $12 — Multiply mentally.

So, the total cost of the notebooks is about $12.

Estimate each product.

1. $0.94
    × 9
    $1 × 9 = $9

2. $3.92
    × 5
    $4 × 5 = $20

3. $3.79
    × 8
    $4 × 8 = $32

4. $2.82
    × 4
    $3 × 4 = $12

5. $7.25
    × 6
    $7 × 6 = $42

6. $2.67
    × 2
    $3 × 2 = $6

7. $1.75
    × 7
    $2 × 7 = $14

8. $68.70
    × 4
    $70 × 4 = $280

9. $9.85
    × 8
    $10 × 8 = $80

10. 20.1
    × 9
    20 × 9 = 180

11. 10.8
    × 7
    11 × 7 = 77

12. 79.3
    × 40
    80 × 40 = 3,200

13. 61.2
    × 5
    60 × 5 = 300

14. 23.4
    × 60
    20 × 60 = 1,200

15. 87.5
    × 42
    90 × 40 = 3,600

Grade 5   43   Chapter 3

3–7 Enrich

Name _____ Date _____

Multiplication Properties

Write two number sentences to show the Commutative Property of Multiplication. Then shade the grids to show the number sentences you wrote.

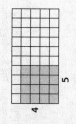

4 × 5 = 20   5 × 4 = 20

Write a number sentence to show the Identity Property of Multiplication. Then shade the grid to show the number sentence you wrote.

1 × 17 = 17

Write a number sentence to show the Distributive Property. Then shade the grid to show the number sentence you wrote.

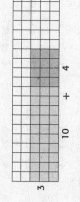

$3 \times (10 + 4) = (3 \times 10) + (3 \times 4) = 30 + 12 = 42$

Grade 5   42   Chapter 3

Answers (Lesson 3–8)

Name _____ Date _____

3-8 Homework Practice
Extending Multiplication

Estimate each product.

1. $5.27
$\times\ 6$
$\$5 \times 6 = \$30$

2. $3.36
$\times\ 4$
$\$3 \times 4 = \$12$

3. $12.17
$\times\ 7$
$\$12 \times 7 = \$84$

4. $4.28
$\times\ 5$
$\$4 \times 5 = \$20$

5. $8.17
$\times\ 8$
$\$8 \times 8 = \$64$

6. $1.32
$\times\ 5$
$\$1 \times 5 = \$5$

7. $27.64
$\times\ 3$
$\$30 \times 3 = \$90$

8. $63.44
$\times\ 6$
$\$60 \times 6 = \$360$

9. $17.55
$\times\ 9$
$\$20 \times 9 = \$180$

10. 7.7
$\times\ 4$
$8 \times 4 = 32$

11. 11.9
$\times\ 21$
$12 \times 20 = 240$

12. 51.7
$\times\ 9$
$50 \times 9 = 450$

13. 33.3
$\times\ 33$
$30 \times 30 = 900$

14. 87.2
$\times\ 41$
$90 \times 40 = 3,600$

15. 17.6
$\times\ 51$
$20 \times 50 = 1,000$

16. 27.1
$\times\ 205$
$30 \times 200 = 6,000$

17. 72.1
$\times\ 51$
$70 \times 50 = 3,500$

18. 92.1
$\times\ 11$
$90 \times 10 = 900$

Spiral Review

Use properties of multiplication to find each product mentally. Show your steps and identify the properties that you used. (Lesson 3-7)

19. $5 \times 14 \times 2$
$5 \times 2 \times 14$ Commutative
$(5 \times 2) \times 14$ Associative
10×14 Find 5×2 mentally.
140 Find 10×14 mentally.

20. $50 \times 6 \times 20$
$50 \times 20 \times 6$ Commutative
$(50 \times 20) \times 6$ Associative
1000×6 Find 50×20 mentally.
$6,000$ Find $1,000 \times 6$ mentally.

Grade 5   45   Chapter 3

Name _____ Date _____

3-8 Skills Practice
Extending Multiplication

Estimate each product.

1. $1.80
$\times\ 8$
$\$2 \times 8 = \$16$

2. $2.83
$\times\ 7$
$\$3 \times 7 = \$21$

3. $14.75
$\times\ 4$
$\$15 \times 4 = \$60$

4. $31.15
$\times\ 4$
$\$30 \times 4 = \$120$

5. $4.80
$\times\ 5$
$\$5 \times 5 = \$25$

6. $1.67
$\times\ 4$
$\$2 \times 4 = \$8$

7. $1.79
$\times\ 6$
$\$2 \times 6 = \$12$

8. $2.26
$\times\ 14$
$\$2 \times 14 = \$28$

9. $9.72
$\times\ 15$
$\$10 \times 15 = \$150$

10. 8.4
$\times\ 41$
$8 \times 40 = 320$

11. 48.2
$\times\ 31$
$50 \times 30 = 1,500$

12. 14.7
$\times\ 305$
$15 \times 300 = 4,500$

13. 42.3
$\times\ 31$
$40 \times 30 = 1,200$

14. 104.6
$\times\ 411$
$100 \times 400 = 40,000$

15. 21.3
$\times\ 72$
$20 \times 70 = 1,400$

Solve.

16. Each Sunday during his nine week summer vacation, Ray buys a newspaper. The Sunday paper costs $1.85. About how much did Ray spend on the Sunday newspaper during his vacation?

$9 \times \$2 = \$18$

17. Jorge buys 8 pounds of ground beef for $3.29 a pound. About how much did he pay altogether?

$8 \times \$3 = \$24$

Grade 5   44   Chapter 3

Answers (Lesson 3–8)

3-8

Name _____ Date _____

Problem-Solving Practice

Extending Multiplication

Solve.

1. Andrea earns $32.00 a day. After 9 days, about how much will she have earned?

   $270

2. Constantino bought 7 pounds of mozzarella cheese. Each pound costs $4.29. About how much did he spend altogether?

   $28

3. Kasi is traveling in the United States. If the exchange rate is 58 rupees for every American dollar, about how many rupees does it take to purchase a meal that costs $12.98?

   600 rupees

4. A school receives $14.00 for every 1,000 labels they collect from certain products. About how much money will they make if students collect 3,000 labels?

   $42

5. In Spanish class, Kevin learns an average of 34 new words per month. If he takes Spanish for 3 years, about how many words will he learn?

   1,080 words

6. An amusement park charges $35.50 for admission. On one day, 6,789 people visited the park. About how much money did the park make from admission that day?

   $280,000

Chapter Resources

3-8

Name _____ Date _____

Enrich

Extending Multiplication

Find each product to decode a secret message.

D	W	E	A
$5.70 × 34	$4.21 × 9	875 × 63	563 ×70
L	**U**	**I**	**Y**
$5.66 × 13	$7.19 × 34	89 × 876	123 × 342
P	**C**	**N**	**M**
$52.88 × 644	$32.99 × 211	65 × 65	$7.66 × 55
O	**H**	**S**	**G**
$12.44 × 555	2,233 × 155	$1.39 × 45	29 × 34
T	**I**	**O**	**T**
75 × 78		$6.75 × 555	129 × 75
		$45.85 × 25	

Match the letter in each box with one of the products below the lines. Write the letter on the line.

	W				T	H
	$37.89	77,964	5,850	346,115
D		**E**	**C**	**I**	**M**	**A**	**L**	**S**
$193.80	55,125	$6,960.89	$1,146.25	$421.30	39,410	$73.58	$62.55
Y	**O**	**U**	**G**	**E**	**T**		
42,066	$3,746.25	$244.46	986	55,125	5,850		
T	**H**	**E**	**P**	**O**	**I**	**N**	**T**
9,675	346,115	$34,054.72	$6,904.2	77,964	4,225	9,675

Answers

3-9

Name _____ Date _____

Reteach

Problem-Solving Investigation: Extra or Missing Information

Benjamin was in charge of selling tickets to the school play. On Monday he sold 10 tickets. He sold 8 tickets on Tuesday and again on Wednesday. On Thursday he sold 10 tickets, and on Friday he sold 5. The play was on Saturday at noon.

Find the amount of money Benjamin collected selling tickets to the school play.

Understand	**What facts do you know?** You know how many tickets Benjamin sold Monday–Friday. You also know when the play was. **What do you need to find?** How much money Benjamin collected selling tickets to the school play.
Plan	**Is there any information that is not needed?** The day and time of the play **Is there any information that is missing?** You do not know the cost of a ticket.
Solve	Since you do not have enough information, the problem cannot be solved.
Check	Read the question again to see if you missed any information. If so, go back and rework the problem. If not, the problem cannot be solved.

Solve each problem. If there is extra information, identify it. If there is not enough information, tell what information is needed.

1. Julia drinks 5 glasses of water on day 1 and 4 glasses of water on day 2. She also drank 4 glasses of water on day 3. She drank 7 glasses on day 4. She also had some juice on day 4. What is the total number of glasses of water she drank at the end of the four days.

   Julia drank 20 glasses total on the 4 days. The fact that Julia also had some juice on day 4 is extra information.

3-9

Name _____ Date _____

Reteach

Problem-Solving Investigation: Extra or Missing Information *(continued)*

Solve each problem. If there is extra information, identify it. If there is not enough information, tell what information is needed.

2. Susan bikes 3 miles round-trip from home to school, Monday through Friday. On Saturday and Sunday she does not ride her bike, but skateboards around her neighborhood. How many miles total does she bike to and from school each week?

   Susan bikes 15 miles total to and from school each week. The fact that Susan skateboards on the weekend is extra information.

3. Jason's goal is to wash 30 cars on the day of his scout troop's car wash fundraiser. If he washes 5 cars between 9:00 and 11:00 A.M. and 10 more cars between noon and 2:30, will he meet his goal?

   The problem cannot be solved because there is not enough information provided.

4. Carl is planting an herb garden. If his garden has 3 rows and he can plant three herbs in each row, how many herbs can he grow?

   9 herbs

5. Mr. Davis has too much stuff so he is having a yard sale. He wants to make at least $200 from the sale. If he has sold $20 worth of his belongings to five different people, has he reached his goal?

   Mr. Davis has not reached his goal. He has only earned $100. We do not need to know that Mr. Davis has too much stuff.

6. Marissa can run 1 mile in 10 minutes. How many miles will she run in a half hour?

   3 mi

7. Zach really enjoys listening to music. If Zach listens to 3 hours of music a day, how many total hours of music will he listen to in 7 days?

   21 hours. It is not necessary to know that Zach really enjoys listening to music.

3-9 Skills Practice

Problem-Solving Investigation: Extra or Missing Information

Name _____ **Date** _____

Solve each problem. If there is extra information, identify it. If there is not enough information, tell what information is needed.

1. Mrs. Blackwell gives each of her students two pencils. How many pencils did she hand out?

missing information: The problem cannot be solved because the number of students is unknown.

2. Mary has saved $50. If she wants to buy an mp3 player that costs $250, will she have enough money in six months?

missing information: The problem cannot be solved because you don't know how much she will be saving, per month, during the next six months' time.

3. Marco does 10 extra math problems each school night. How many extra problems does he do each school week?

50 problems

4. Juan's family is from Houston. They want to go to Florida for vacation. If they need $100 for each person in the family in order to be able to make the trip, will they have enough?

extra and missing information. You do not need to know where Juan's family is from in order to solve the problem. You do need to know how many people are in Juan's family and how much money they have for the vacation in order to be able to solve the problem.

5. Shannon has five red shirts, three blue shirts, and four purple shirts. She has three more white shirts than she does brown shirts. How many brown shirts does she have?

missing information: The problem cannot be solved because you don't know how many white or brown shirts Shannon has.

6. If David plays 3 tennis matches every week for 9 weeks, how many matches will he play altogether?

27 matches

3-9 Homework Practice

Problem-Solving Investigation

Name _____ **Date** _____

Solve each problem. If there is extra information, identify it. If there is not enough information, tell what information is needed.

1. The Alvarez family bought a car for $2,000. They made a down payment of $500. If they want to pay the balance in five equal payments, how much will each of these payments be?

$300

2. Melanie can walk five miles in a half hour. How many miles will she walk in one week?

missing information: You need to know how many many miles Melanie walks each day in order to answer the question.

3. Jamie and Melissa both have 30 CDs. How many more CDs does John have?

missing information: You need to know how many CDs John owns.

4. Anna collected 50 cans for a food drive. She collected 10 cans each day of the drive, mostly green beans. How many days did she collect cans?

Anna collected canned food for 5 days. Extra information: You don't need to know that Anna collected more green beans than any other kind of canned food.

Spiral Review

Estimate.

5. $6.82
$$\times\ 4$$
$$\$7 \times 4 = \$28$$

6. $3.37
$$\times\ 2$$
$$\$3 \times 2 = \$6$$

7. $41.64
$$\times\ 12$$
$$\$40 \times 10 = \$400$$

8. $35.61
$$\times\ 24$$
$$\$40 \times 20 = \$800$$

9. $17.52
$$\times\ 18$$
$$\$20 \times 20 = 400$$

10. 2.67
$$\times\ 54$$
$$3 \times 50 = 150$$

11. 94.2
$$\times\ 76$$
$$90 \times 80 = 7,200$$

12. 76.4
$$\times\ 127$$
$$80 \times 100 = 8,000$$

13. 8.6
$$\times\ 82$$
$$9 \times 80 = 720$$

Answers

Answers (Lesson 3-9 and Vocabulary Test)

Name _____ Date _____

3 Vocabulary Test

Match each word to its definition. Write your answers on the lines provided.

1. cluster __B__	A. The answer to a multiplication problem.
2. Distributive Property __D__	B. group together
3. factor __E__	C. The property which states that the grouping of the factors does not change the product.
4. product __A__	D. The property that states that to multiply a sum by a number, you can multiply each addend by the same number and add the products.
5. Associative Property __C__	E. A number that divides into a whole number evenly. Also, a number that is multiplied by another number.

Grade 5   60   Chapter 3

Name _____ Date _____

3-9 Enrich
Extra or Missing Information

Use the chart to solve the problems. If there is not enough information to solve, write *not enough information* and tell what information is needed. If you can estimate the missing information, write *estimate*, and explain your estimate. If there is too much information, write *too much information* and tell what information you need to solve the problem.

Rebecca's school will order sports caps with the school name. She is taking color requests from her classmates. She has 40 requests so far.

Sports Caps	
Color	**Number of Students**
Red	4
Blue	12
Black	16
White	8

1. Rebecca plans to take 10 more requests. What fraction of the requests did she already have for red caps?

   Too much information; need the total number of orders so far and the number of red caps ordered so far; $\frac{1}{10}$

2. Rebecca just added 8 more requests. Now what fraction of the total requests are for black caps?

   Not enough information; need to know the number of caps that are black in the new orders.

3. If Rebecca takes 50 requests, how many will be for white caps?

   Estimate; 40 or $\frac{1}{5}$ of the caps are white now, so about $\frac{1}{5}$ of 50 should be white after she takes 50 orders; 10 white caps

4. The blue and the red caps costs $1.50 more than the black and the white caps. What is the total cost of the blue caps requested?

   Not enough information; need to know the cost of the black and white caps.

5. The blue caps cost $5.50 each and the black caps cost $4.00 each. What is the total cost of the black caps requested so far?

   Too much information; need the total number of black caps ordered and the cost of the black caps; $64

Grade 5   52   Chapter 3

Name _____ Date _____

3 **Oral Assessment**

For this activity, gather a box of 100 paper clips or a similar number of other small objects and model for the student the concept of arranging the objects into smaller groups and using the Distributive Property to aid with mental multiplication.

Read each question aloud to the student. The student should rearrange the objects into smaller groups. Then write the student's answers on the lines below the question.

1. If you want to multiply 6 × 16, how many groups of 6 objects should you make?

16

2. How can you separate 16 into two numbers that are easier to multiply by 6? What two groups of objects do you now have?

16 easily splits into 10 and 6. That leaves 10 groups of 6 and 6 groups of 6.

3. What is 6 × 10?

60

4. What is 6 × 6

36

5. What is 60 + 36?

96

6. Write the original problem using the Distributive Property.

(6 × 10) + (6 × 6) = 96

Name _____ Date _____

3 **Oral Assessment** *(continued)*

For the word problem that follows, the student will need to draw a square that is 12 in. × 12 in. on a piece of paper and divide the square horizontally into 1-in. increments. Work through the word problem with the student by reading each question aloud and writing the student's answer on the lines that follow.

Farmer McAllister has a plot of land that is 12 feet long by 12 feet wide. He wants to plant 3 rows of lettuce, 4 rows of tomatoes, and 2 rows of beans. Each row of vegetables is 1 foot wide and 12 feet long, and in between each crop, he must leave 1 foot of empty soil. Does he have enough room in his plot of land to plant all the rows of vegetables he desires?

7. What facts do you know about the plot of land?

It is 12 feet long and 12 feet wide. Farmer McAllister wants to plant a total of 9 rows of vegetables. There must be 1 empty foot of soil between each of the 3 crops.

8. Look at the square on the paper in front of you. How many rows do you see?

12

9. How many total rows of space will the vegetables need to grow?

9

10. How many total rows of empty soil will he need?

1 row in between the lettuce and tomatoes and 1 row in between the tomatoes and the beans; 2 rows total

11. If you add up the empty rows and the rows of vegetables, does Farmer McAllister have enough room on his plot of land?

9 rows of vegetables + 2 rows of empty soil = 11 rows total: since 11 is less than 12, Farmer McAllister does have enough room for his crops.

Answers

Chapter 3 Assessment Answer Key

Chapter Diagnostic Test
Page 54

1. _____36_____
2. _____30_____
3. _____25_____
4. _____48_____
5. _____4_____
6. _____63_____
7. _____28 in._____

8. ___5 × 8; 40___
9. ___6 × 6; $36___
10. ___2 × 8; 16___
11. ___7 × 8; 56___

12. _____35,407_____
13. _____2,589_____
14. _____15,048_____
15. _____5,768_____

Chapter Pretest
Page 55

1. _____400_____
2. _____33,000_____
   (3 × 40) + (3 × 4);
3. _____132_____
4. **(7 × 20) + (7 × 8); 196**
5. ___30 × 20 = 600___
6. __100 × 40 = 4,000__
7. _____81 90_____
8. _____588_____
9. _____864_____
10. _____5,356_____
11. _____Identity_____
12. ____Commutative____
13. ___$6 × 3 = $18___
14. __60 × 40 = 2,400__
15. **missing information: the number of party guests**

Quiz 1
Page 56

1. _____240_____
2. _____64,000_____
3. **280 swimmers**
4. **2 × (50 + 4) = (2 × 50) + (2 × 4) = 100 + 8 = 108**
5. **(60 + 7) × 4 = (60 × 4) + (7 × 4) = 240 + 28 = 268**
6. **70 × 50 = 3,500**
7. **400 × 30 = 12,000**
8. **4 × $3.00 = $12.00**

Chapter 3 Assessment Answer Key

Quiz 2
Page 57

1. ____371____

2. ___1,893___

3. __204 pounds__

4. __5 awards;__
   __5 inches__

5. ___1,332___

6. ___12,291___

7. ____$495____

Quiz 3
Page 58

1. __Associative__

2. __Commutative__

3. _$5 × 20 = $100_

4. _$10 × 7 = $70_

5. _6 × 12 = 72_

6. ___$17.43___

7. __$210; extra__
   __information:__
   __Mark is__
   __bringing 3__
   __friends with__
   __him to the__
   __concert.__

8. __missing__
   __information:__
   __number of__
   __problems__
   __completed per__
   __hour__

Mid-Chapter Test
Page 59

1. ____280____

2. __120,000__

3. $3 \times (70 + 2) =$
   $(3 \times 70) + (3 \times 2) =$
   $210 + 6 = 216$

4. $(90 + 4) \times 6 =$
   $(90 \times 6) + (4 \times 6) =$
   $540 + 24 = 564$

5. $20 \times 90 = 1{,}800$

6. $500 \times 4 = 2{,}000$

7. ____201____

8. ___1,712___

Answers

Chapter 3 Assessment Answer Key

Chapter Test, Form 1
Page 65

1. **C**

2. **F**

3. **D**

4. **J**

5. **C**

6. **F**

7. **C**

8. **G**

9. **B**

10. **H**

11. **C**

Page 66

12. **G**

13. **C**

14. **H**

15. **C**

16. **F**

17. **B**

18. **H**

19. **B**

20. **H**

Chapter Test, Form 2A
Page 67

1. **C**

2. **F**

3. **A**

4. **F**

5. **C**

6. **G**

7. **C**

8. **G**

9. **B**

10. **H**

11. **B**

(continued on the next page)

Chapter 3 Assessment Answer Key

Chapter Test, Form 2A
(continued)

Page 68

12. __H__

13. __C__

14. __H__

15. __A__

16. __G__

17. __B__

18. __J__

19. __B__

20. __H__

Chapter Test, Form 2B

Page 69

1. __C__

2. __F__

3. __A__

4. __F__

5. __C__

6. __G__

7. __C__

8. __G__

9. __B__

10. __H__

11. __B__

Page 70

12. __H__

13. __C__

14. __H__

15. __A__

16. __G__

17. __B__

18. __H__

19. __B__

20. __H__

Answers

Chapter 3 Assessment Answer Key

Chapter Test, Form 2C
Page 71

1. 2,400
2. 6,000
3. 72
4. 42
5. $78
6. 288 pages
7. 120
8. $32,000
9. 492
10. $9,086
11. 187
12. 216 chairs
13. 14

Page 72

14. 8
15. 392 desks
16. $2 × 8 = $16
17. 2 × 50 = 100
18. 312 crayons
19. $20
20. 13 DVDs

Chapter Test, Form 2D
Page 73

1. 2,400
2. 6,000
3. 72
4. 42
5. $78
6. 288 pages
7. 120
8. $32,000
9. 492
10. $9,086
11. 187
12. 216 chairs
13. 14

(continued on the next page)

Chapter 3 Assessment Answer Key

Chapter Test, Form 2D
(continued)
Page 74

14. _____ **8**

15. _____ **392 desks**

16. **$2 × 8 = $16**

17. **2 × 50 = 100**

18. **312 crayons**

19. _____ **$20**

20. _____ **13 DVDs**

Chapter Test, Form 3
Page 75

1. _____ **24,000**

2. _____ **6,000**

3. _____ **76**

4. _____ **81**

5. _____ **$81**

6. **1,188 pages**

7. _____ **120**

8. **$34,400**

9. _____ **492**

10. **$22,066**

11. _____ **187**

12. **264 chairs**

13. _____ **14**

Page 76

14. _____ **8**

15. _____ **486 desks**

16. **$2 × 8 = 16**

17. **2 × 50 = 100**

18. **338 crayons**

19. _____ **$20**

20. _____ **13 DVDs**

Answers

Chapter 3 Assessment Answer Key

Page 77, Chapter Extended-Response Test
Scoring Rubric

Level	Specific Criteria
4	The student demonstrates a ***thorough understanding*** of the mathematics concepts and/or procedures embodied in the task. The student has responded correctly to the task, used mathematically sound procedures, and provided clear and complete explanations and interpretations. The response may contain minor flaws that do not detract from the demonstration of a thorough understanding.
3	The student demonstrates an ***understanding*** of the mathematics concepts and/or procedures embodied in the task. The student's response to the task is essentially correct, with the mathematical procedures used and the explanations and interpretations provided demonstrating an essential but less than thorough understanding. The response may contain minor errors that reflect inattentive execution of the mathematical procedures or indications of some misunderstanding of the underlying mathematics concepts and/or procedures.
2	The student has demonstrated only a ***partial understanding*** of the mathematics concepts and/or procedures embodied in the task. Although the student may have used the correct approach to obtaining a solution or may have provided a correct solution, the student's work lacks an essential understanding of the underlying mathematical concepts. The response contains errors related to misunderstanding important aspects of the task, misuse of mathematical procedures, or faulty interpretations of results.
1	The student has demonstrated a ***very limited understanding*** of the mathematics concepts and/or procedures embodied in the task. The student's response to the task is incomplete and exhibits many flaws. Although the student has addressed some of the conditions of the task, the student reached an inadequate conclusion and/or provided reasoning that was faulty or incomplete. The response exhibits many errors or may be incomplete.
0	The student has provided a ***completely incorrect*** solution or uninterpretable response, or no response at all.

Chapter 3 Assessment Answer Key

Page 77, Chapter Extended-Response Test
Sample Answers

In addition to the scoring rubric found on page A32, the following sample answers may be used as guidance in evaluating open-ended assessment items.

1. You can use mental math by first multiplying 5 and 6 and getting 30. Then you know you need to add 4 more zeros to the end of 30, getting 300,000. Finally, you need to multiply 300,000 by 2, and you get 600,000. This uses the distributive property. Another way you can find this answer mentally is by first multiplying 50 and 2 to get 100. Then you multiply 6,000 by 100 by adding two zeros to the end, and you get 600,000. This uses the distributive property.

2. **a.** The museum has already sold 1,560 tickets.

    b. The museum needs to make $17,280 more in August.

    c. 1,440 tickets still need to be sold.

Answers

Chapter 3 Assessment Answer Key

Cumulative Test Practice Chapters 1–3

Page 78

1. __**B**__

2. __**F**__

3. __**B**__

Page 79

4. __**J**__

5. __**B**__

6. __**H**__

7. __**A**__

8. __**H**__

Page 80

9. __**D**__

10. __**J**__

11. __**64**__

12. __**276**__

13. __**84**__

14. __**24**__

15. __**26**__